EATING MATTERS

Why We Eat What We Eat

Gerald Bennett

HEINEMANN KINGSWOOD

Heinemann Kingswood
Michelin House, 81 Fulham Road, London SW3 6RB

LONDON   MELBOURNE
JOHANNESBURG   AUCKLAND

ISBN 0 434 98138 9 (cased)
ISBN 0 434 98162 1 (paper)

Photoset by Deltatype Ltd, Ellesmere Port, Cheshire
Printed and bound in Great Britain by
Billing & Sons Ltd, Worcester

Acknowledgements

I should like to thank Eileen MacAlonan for her critical comments on preliminary drafts of this book and Dr Sandra Warrington for protecting me from making too many errors about nutritional matters. Barbara Ayres provided an excess of tasteless suggestions for the title of the book, but provides a living embodiment of the pleasures of eating. My greatest debt is to my wife Vanessa, for supporting me in this project, which has taken me away for many hours from her and from our daughter Lindsay.

The dietary restraint questionnaire (on p. 84) is copyright (1978) of the American Psychological Association and is reprinted by permission of the publisher and authors. The questionnaire measuring oral optimism and pessimism (on p. 137) is reproduced from the Journal of Genetic Psychology, 136, 85–94, 1980, with permission of the Helen Dwight Reid Educational Foundation. Published by Heldref Publications, 4000 Albemarle St, N.W., Washington, DC, 20016 USA. Copyright © 1980.

This book is dedicated to my mother, Peggy Bennett

Contents

Introduction

There is no need to journey to the Amazon jungles or the South Sea Islands to see just how extraordinary human beings are; just go to your nearest supermarket. Stand at the checkouts and look into shoppers' baskets to see which foods they have chosen. Walk around the aisles and watch people deciding what to buy.

The first thing to strike you is the wide variety of foods that people choose, even when similar amounts of money are being spent on similar sized families. The same bill provides one shopper with a basket of vegetables, fruit and meat, but another with a heap of frozen chips, pizzas and biscuits. Some shoppers buy only traditional foods, that were easily available fifty years ago; others also buy exotic spices and foods from other parts of the world – pitta bread, poppadoms, vine leaves and green peppers. Many buy foods – such as yoghurt and muesli – that only twenty years ago had a 'crank' image, but which today are widely accepted. Some buy tripe and cods' roes, others hamburgers and pot noodles. Why should one person differ so much from another? Are we all born with different tastes, or do these differences develop out of our

1

experiences of life? Can parents guide or influence the likes and dislikes of their children, who stand beside them in the queue at the checkout? Children are strongly drawn to sweet foods such as the chocolate bars for sale at the checkout. Why should this be? It seems strange that nature should attract us to foods that harm us, such as the sugary foods which contribute to tooth decay and many illnesses.

Some trollies at the checkout are full of low-calorie foods, such as low-fat margarines, grapefruits, saccharin tablets, and low-calorie drinks, soups, and biscuits. Other trollies are full of foods concentrated with energy, such as ice cream, chips and cakes. There are generally no conspicuous differences in weight between people buying high-calorie food and those buying low-calorie food. Overweight people buy 'slimming food' to help them lose weight; thin people buy it to help them stay thin. The foods people choose show their concern about weight; their conflicting feelings are tapped by advertisements such as that for cream cakes headed 'Naughty – but nice'.

While dieters check labels to see how many calories the food contains, some parents are checking them for a very different reason. They are making sure that the food doesn't contain particular artificial additives which they believe affect the way their children behave. They believe that eating foods containing some dyes and preservatives will cause the well-behaved child beside them to change personality, and become impulsive, over-active and disobedient. Are they correct to believe this? Is their effort worth it?

Other shoppers are buying products specifically in order to affect their behaviour. Some poor sleepers are choosing malted milk drinks to help them get off to sleep at night. Why should milky drinks have this effect? And why should other foods, such as coffee, have the opposite effect?

Shopping for food is an everyday chore that produces few strong feelings in most people – but in a minority it does induce strong emotions such as fear, disgust and guilt. A very thin woman suffering from anorexia nervosa walks round the store feeling detached and superior. Although she appears unhealthily thin to everyone else, she feels that she is overweight and regards food as gross. What causes such a contradictory and puzzling disorder as this? Much less identifiable by her appearance is a young woman afflicted by bulimia nervosa, the disorder that involves alternate fasting, bingeing, and vomiting. Only a tell-tale puffiness in the face gives her away as she fills her basket with 'good' low-calorie foods, together with 'wicked' foods on which she plans to binge later. Her life is dominated by food, and visiting the supermarket is an unsettling experience. What kind of treatment is effective for this disorder?

A recent immigrant from a country with a very different culture examines tins and packets looking for something familiar and appetising. The frozen joints of meat and packets of frozen peas are as unattractive to him as a breakfast of raw fish is to the average Westerner. Why is it so difficult for people to learn to like eating highly nutritious foods that they have never come across before? Why is it so hard to shed feelings of disgust, and to change our likes and dislikes? Why is it so hard to change our eating habits?

This book is about the issues raised by our trip around the supermarket; it is about our eating habits – what they are, how they develop and change, and how they affect our lives. Eating is an extraordinary activity, but we take it so much for granted that we are often unaware of the strangeness of our own eating habits. Eating is extraordinary because it is one of the very few things we have to do in order to stay alive. Eating something is the most intimate contact we can have with anything or anyone; the substances that we swallow are broken down into their most basic molecular forms and literally become part of us. We put something into our mouths to eat 25,000 times a year. In a lifetime the action is repeated some two million times, allowing thirty or forty tons of food to be swallowed. The composition of all this food influences our health and how long we will live.

Eating is so central to our survival that it could not be left just to the rational parts of our minds to control. Our eating habits show how limited the rational side of human beings is.

We believe that we are free to choose what we eat, but this is an illusion. Our choice has been moulded and limited by our experiences from conception onwards. When we look at our eating habits we realise how little they have to do with our rational choices, and how much they are influenced by forces of which we are largely unaware.

In this book we will try to answer the questions raised by our trip around the supermarket with the help of scientific evidence. We do not know all the answers to these questions, but we know a great deal more than we did even twenty years ago. Most of these advances have come from the experiments and detailed studies of scientific psychologists; much of this book is based on their findings. The first chapter is an exception. In it we stand back and take a wider view of human eating habits, such as reactions to famines, which cannot easily be studied through experiments – we need to look at eating habits around the world, today and in the past. In Chapter 2 we look at our instincts, and how far these can make us desire the foods our body needs. We then focus on the ways in which we learn from our experiences with food, both as children (Chapter 3) and as adults (Chapter 4) to like some foods but not others. Chapters 5 and 6 look at the relationship between mind and mouth from opposite directions – how our minds determine our food choices (Chapter 5) and the effects of food on our emotions and behaviour (Chapter 6). Our eating habits are inextricable from other aspects of our lives, and Chapter 7 explores how they are intimately associated with sleeping habits and body rhythms, and examines suggestions that our early eating habits form our character. In Chapter 8 we examine similar claims about our species as a whole – is human nature the way it is because our distant ancestors took up hunting to get food? Finally we consider practical problems of today: obesity and weight reduction (Chapter 9) and eating disorders such as anorexia nervosa (Chapter 10).

So much for the menu – on with the meal!

1

Food habits

Imagine yourself as a castaway, stranded on a very pleasant tropical island where all your needs are catered for – except for food. You have an unlimited supply of small tasteless pills which supply all your nutritional needs, so there is no need to take anything else. But, as on the best desert islands, you have a choice. You can take three types of food with you (either individual items, or complete meals). These three foods will be available whenever you want them. Which three foods would you take? What would be your Desert Island Dishes?

Once you have chosen them you can reflect on your choices. Why those particular foods? Are they ones that you learned to enjoy early in life? When did you first taste them? Have they got particular associations for you – do they remind you of any person, or of any specific time in your life? Is it the flavour of the food that attracts you, or its texture? Have you automatically chosen foods for a balanced diet? Is there a feeling that the food will do you good? Have you chosen an expensive food which you could not normally afford? It is almost certain that you will not have chosen any of the highly nutritious foods that are eaten only outside the Western world.

The variety of foods

There are tens of thousands of species of plants and animals that humans can eat and thrive on, but only a very small proportion of these are actually used as food. Different cultures accept, enjoy, and relish particular species as foods and reject others as either alien or disgusting. The ancient Romans liked to eat doormice and kept them in cages ready for the kitchen. Cannibalism has been practised in many countries, although who eats whom varies from one culture to another. In some societies enemies are eaten, but in others people eat their dead relatives and friends as a gesture of friendship, believing, as one South American Indian put it, that 'it is better to be inside a friend than to be swallowed up by the cold earth.' Insects are eaten by many societies; our distaste is partly explained by our ignorance of the fact that many of their species live on clean vegetation and contain everything we need for a healthy diet. Lightly fried termites, as eaten in Zaire, have much more protein than beef, and dried locusts have even more. In Laos and New Caledonia spiders are eaten as a delicacy. In 1885 a British eccentric, V.M. Holt, published a book entitled *Why not eat insects?*, in which he argued the case for insects as food. He included menus for dinner parties based on insects and summarised his thesis thus: 'The insects eat up every blessed green thing that do grow and us farmers starve. Well, eat them and grow fat!' Holt's case is logical, but food likes and dislikes have little to do with logic.

Any child could at birth be brought up to speak in any of the world's thousands of languages and to adopt it as its mother tongue; in the same way almost any child could be brought up to accept and thrive on any of the hundreds of cuisines that exist. Similarly, the adult who has to put a great deal of effort into learning to speak another language can find it just as difficult to accept and consume the food of another society. The Eskimo, who regards the nose of the caribou as a delicacy, finds it no easier to eat many of the foods available on our supermarket shelves than British people would to consume the cats and dogs relished by the Chinese. Yet the same new-born child could learn to enjoy eating any one of these (or, indeed, all of them).

We like what we know

One of the most striking things about human food likes and dislikes is how fixed they become. As children develop and become adults they become more set in their preferences. Instead of learning to like more and more foods throughout life, people tend to stay with a limited range of familiar dishes: food preferences run deep. Strange and unknown foods are seen as almost taboo, and it is regarded as foolhardy or brave to attempt to eat them. In 1985 British television showed a documentary series about the training of Royal Marine Commandos. Although this showed them carrying out all manner of dangerous tasks – such as climbing sheer cliffs – public attention, including the reviews, centred on one episode in which they ate an omelette of earthworms as part of survival training. This was seen as braver than any of the hazardous actions. The irrational fear or dislike of novel foods is called 'neophobia', the fear of the new. Neophobia is combined with a liking for what is familiar and known.

Such conservatism is most strongly evident in extreme circumstances, such as illness or danger. When unwell in a foreign country, the traveller is likely to reject the novel foods that he adventurously tasted several days before; familiar food, especially food that he has eaten from childhood, is more appealing. The unwell British visitor to Japan is likely to prefer his usual breakfast cereal to the traditional Japanese dish of raw fish. American astronauts took their most familiar foods with them into space – beef and gravy, fried bacon, chicken and cornflakes. The Soviet cosmonauts have always taken fairly normal foods, such as bread, along with high-tech foods such as 'energy pastilles' wrapped in aluminium. A French astronaut, Jean-Loup Chrétien, who ventured into

7

space with the Russians in 1986, complained about their diet, and so French chefs have produced gourmet meals for use in space, complete in containers to be heated up in space microwave ovens.

Soldiers in the combat zone reject novel foods in preference for more familiar ones – even if that familiarity is limited. Studies of American servicemen found that having tasted a strange food just once made all the difference. The food was pemmican, a meat bar, used extensively by hunters, trappers and polar explorers. This was issued as part of emergency rations to aircrew taking part in seven-day survival exercises in remote wilderness areas. Their reactions to it varied enormously; at one extreme, some aircrew tasted it just once and then spat it out, while at the other extreme were men who ate all their pemmican and then acquired more from their fellow crewmen. The main factor determining whether the men accepted or rejected the pemmican was whether or not they had tasted it before. Those who had done so (regardless of how much they had previously eaten or of whether or not they had enjoyed it) ate more pemmican and liked it more. Just tasting it was sufficient.

Starving in the presence of food

Conservatism operates strongly even in emergencies when life is threatened by starvation, and where the need to survive would be expected to override cultural restraints. The most dramatic examples of this are where, in famines, people die because they cannot accept the food that could save them. In 1770 starving inhabitants of Naples refused to eat a cargo of potatoes sent to relieve their famine, because they still regarded this New World crop with suspicion. In one of the greatest famines of the twentieth century, three million people died in Bengal in 1943 when the rice crop failed. In some areas starving people were given wheat, which was totally new to them, but they rejected this and died. In such circumstances providing inappropriate food is often as bad as providing no food at all.

8

During the Great Irish Famine of the 1840s the government had to overcome the same obstacles in attempting to alleviate starvation. The famine was triggered off by recurrent blight on potatoes, the staple food of the Irish. Since its introduction to the island about 150 years before, much of the population depended on this single crop for food, and its success had allowed the population to treble. Other foods were used less and less by peasants, and the means of preparing them became unfamiliar. An English official of the time observed: 'There is scarcely a woman of the peasant class in the West of Ireland whose culinary art exceeds the boiling of a potato. Bread is scarcely ever seen, and an oven is unknown.' The failure of the potato crop had such a grave impact because of this dependence on a single vegetable, and within ten years a third of the population had died or emigrated. The British Government's Relief Commission for Ireland imported Indian corn (maize) from America; this had never been used as a food in the British Isles before. At first there was widespread rejection of the bright yellow ground corn, dubbed 'Peel's brimstone' after the Prime Minister and its resemblance to sulphur. So great was the reaction that in some areas starving inmates of workhouses refused to eat it, and riots occurred. Only when the famine reached its most severe and deadly level was the meal gradually accepted.

It is extremely difficult for us to overcome our reluctance to eat strange foods; education and rational thought have little effect. During the Second World War American pilots in the Pacific were given survival training which taught them which nutritious plants and animals they could safely eat if they were forced down. Yet, in the event, many went hungry rather than dine on unfamiliar reptiles, insects, or plants. The constraints on rational thought overcoming such deeply ingrained taboos were vividly and poignantly illustrated in 1972 when an aircraft carrying a Uruguayan college rugby team and supporters crashed in a remote spot in the Argentinian Andes. Twenty-eight survivors were stranded virtually without food in sub-zero temperatures in one of the most isolated and

9

inhospitable places on earth. The only nutritious material for them to survive on was the flesh of their dead companions, but it took them ten days of hunger and cold to make the decision to eat this. They had no moral objection to it, but a deep physical revulsion, which they overcame only when death was near. They found it easier to eat their friends' bodies when they viewed this act in religious terms, as being akin to Holy Communion, when the worshipper consumes Christ's body. This act of cannibalism enabled sixteen of them to survive for a further sixty-two days until they were rescued. Food habits run so deep that even this highly educated and sophisticated group nearly died of starvation before taking what they saw as the rational step. The oldest was the last to eat. Even when survival is at stake food habits retain their grip.

Neophobia in the modern world

Neophobia and the liking for familiar foods may seem to be distant from the changing food patterns we have seen in the West in recent decades, with the introduction of many foods from other parts of the world. It is true that conservatism cannot be the whole story, but it can easily be underestimated. One of the most notable trends in the West has been the spread of standardised tastes, particularly in fast foods. If you go under the golden arch into a McDonalds anywhere in the world the decor is the same, the range of foods available is the same, and the taste of the food is the same. The outstanding popularity of standard food is due to its familiarity. Only the very rich, such as the Queen of England, can afford to take their usual food with them wherever they go. (When the Queen goes on overseas visits she takes shortbread, Harrods sausages, China and Indian tea, mint sauce, jam, barley sugar, Malvern water and fruitcake.) Eating in a 'standard food' restaurant is the commoner's way of doing the same as the Queen.

The dislike of change is shown in the unexpected resistance to change in the extremely popular beverage, Coca-Cola.

Coca-Cola is the best-selling drink in the world, selling twice as much as its nearest rival. Since its invention by a pharmacist in Atlanta, Georgia in 1886, the flavour of the drink remained the same and the formula of the secret ingredient 'Merchandise 7x' was kept secure in a bank vault. Then in April 1985 the company announced that 'the best has been made even better' and introduced 'New Coke', a sweeter drink containing the new flavour ingredient 'Merchandise 7x-100'. New Coke was to replace the old variety. The public response was immediate in rejecting the new brand; the company received 1,500 protesting telephone calls in one day. All over America enthusiastic Coke drinkers stockpiled old Coke. Pressure groups such as the 'Old Coke Drinkers of America' sprang up, led by such charismatic figures as Gay Mullins, a fifty-seven-year-old estate agent who spent $100,000, his life savings, on legal action against the company. Coca-Cola's rival, Pepsi-Cola, celebrated by giving its staff a day off. After eighty-seven days Coca-Cola relented and announced that the old drink (now called 'Classic Coke') would survive and be sold along with 'New Coke'. The American Senator who broke the news to the Senate described the reprieve as 'a very meaningful moment in the history of America'. Within a year Classic Coke was still outselling New Coke by four to one and was the only brand sold by restaurant chains such as McDonalds and Kentucky Fried Chicken. The expensive failure of New Coke seemed astonishing because thorough market research involving 200,000 consumers over three years had predicted success. It is not so surprising when seen as an example of neophobia. As the Coca-Cola President later admitted, the market research did not 'measure or reveal the deep and abiding emotional attachment to original Coca-Cola'. The four million dollars spent on researching the unsuccessful brand was the price of neophobia.

Food habits persist through life

Food likes and dislikes established in childhood can persist through life. Childhood experiences often dictate the food choices made throughout a lifetime. Early experiences of deprivation can influence a lifetime's behaviour. That food habits persist can clearly be seen in immigrants trying to adapt to the way of life of their adopted nation. Although they may gradually change in many ways, speaking a new language, wearing new clothes, and even acquiring new social and political ideas, the last part of their old life to change (if indeed it does) is the cuisine. In Britain, immigrants from India and Pakistan buy imported tropical fruit and vegetables at great expense. As the novelist Anthony Burgess has noted: 'We are finally loyal to the food of our youth, and this is perhaps what patriotism means.' In exile in Italy Burgess cooks the food that he ate in his boyhood in Manchester – Lancashire hotpot, meat and potato pie, and steak pie with cowheel. The old ways are transmitted to the second and third generations of immigrants in the new country, and are only gradually modified and weakened. It may take several generations before the food of the new nation is accepted as 'normal' in the home, unless it can be incorporated into the old cuisine by, for example, the use of traditional flavourings.

Vietnamese immigrants into the USA were able to accept many American foods once they were able to produce traditional fish sauces to flavour them with, so as to transform them into something familiar. In countries such as the USA, where many families have been there only a few generations, the best way of discovering a person's ethnic roots is to look in his kitchen. Even today, when with the diffusion of cooking styles, the wok and pasta-maker are no longer rarities and oregano and pitta bread seem exotic no more, the pattern of ingredients, utensils, and cooking techniques provides a very strong clue. The food that a family eats when it gets together for a special occasion reflects its origins. Studies in Israel, also a nation of newcomers, show the persistence of food habits. First-generation families from Europe eat very few of the wide variety of novel local vegetables and fruit available in the semi-tropical climate; succeeding generations slowly incorporate them. Types of bread and cooking fat are even slower to change, but the types of food most resistant to change are spices, which contribute to the overall distinctive flavour of the meal.

Flavours make foods familiar

Flavours matter most because these convey the most distinctive and familiar character of a cuisine, pervading many foods. Most traditional cuisines have distinctive flavour combinations that 'mark' dishes. In China it is soy sauce, rice wine and ginger root, while in North East Africa it is garlic, cumin and mint. Below is a list of flavour combinations and regions. Can you match them up correctly?

Table 1   Taste combinations used in the cuisines of different regions
Which goes with which?

Taste combination	Region
A Olive oil, lemon, & oregano	1 Korea
B Chilli and tomato	2 Provence
C Olive oil, garlic, parsley and anchovy	3 Japan
D Lemon and parsley	4 North India
E Soy sauce, chilli, brown sugar and sesame seed	5 West Africa
F Soy sauce, garlic, chilli, molasses and peanuts	6 Eastern Europe
G Soured cream and dill or paprika	7 Greece
H Tomato, chilli and peanuts	8 Middle East
I Soy sauce, sugar and rice wine	9 Mexico
J Cumin, ginger and garlic, plus other spices	10 South Italy and France
K Rosemary, sage, marjoram, olive oil and thyme	11 Indonesia

The answers are given on p. 199

It is as hard to think of an Italian meal spiced with curry as it is to imagine a Chinese stir-fried meal containing tomato and oregano. New ingredients can be more easily assimilated if they are 'marked' by the traditional flavour combination. Not all cultures have distinctive flavour combinations; Britain has none and the historical reasons for this are complex.

The persistence of food habits passes unnoticed in normal undisturbed life, but is often highlighted by transitions, crises, and other disturbances. An example of such is when new families are formed from divorce and remarriage. Two partners, each with children and expectations about domestic life (including expectations about meals), combine together to form a new family. Merging together two sets of food habits is one of the recurring areas of difficulty. Nothing exposes the divisions in some families more than the rejection of a step-parent's meals as being 'not what we're used to'. Integration at mealtimes is an important part of family integration. In families as well as in nations, what you eat tells you who you are.

The effects of deprivation

The experience of chronic hunger or deprivation of food can have effects that last throughout life. Physical growth can be permanently affected, as it is in many Third World countries today. During the great siege of Paris in 1870 and 1871 the inhabitants lived under famine conditions. This showed up when those conceived and born in Paris during the siege ('*les enfants du siège*') were recruited to the French Army in the 1890s and proved to be considerably shorter than previous recruits. The psychological effects of chronic hunger can be just as striking. Insecurity about food supply and hoarding food are common after-effects. A poignant example of the long-term effects of food privation is the case of the late Anna Anderson (latterly Manahan), who many people believe was the Grand Duchess Anastasia, daughter of Nicholas II, the last Tsar of Russia. The Tsar and most of his family were executed following the 1917 Russian Revolution, but there were persistent rumours that Anastasia had escaped. Anna Anderson came to light in 1920 in Berlin, exhausted, mentally confused, and chronically malnourished. Whoever she was, she had suffered great deprivation of food during her travels across Europe. During succeeding decades her identity was the object of much controversy as some sought to prove, and others to disprove, that she was in fact Anastasia. The claims to both the Romanov succession and the Imperial wealth deposited in the West depended on this. Even now after sixty-five years and litigation extending over thirty-two of them, her identity is still a controversy. In 1968 she married a retired American professor of history and moved to a relatively prosperous life in Virginia. Despite this security she continued to worry about the sufficiency of food and, every autumn, pulled piles of potatoes into the house in case of a hungry winter. Experience of privation can have lifelong effects.

Food habits resist change by external influence

It is often very difficult for people to voluntarily change their own food habits, even if they very much want to. Most people who try to lose weight by dieting fail, however strongly motivated they are. Old habits tend to supplant new ones, especially under stress; eating habits and food preferences are particularly resistant to change. It is even more difficult for governments and other authorities to influence people to eat differently against their will. History is full of examples where such efforts have been unsuccessful.

Sumptuary laws

In the fourteenth century, after the Black Death and the Plague had killed a quarter of Europe's population, there were problems with food supply. The kings of England and France attempted to solve them by passing laws regulating the consumption of particular foods. These 'Sumptuary Laws' restricted who could eat what and when, and were partly an attempt to keep people in the fixed place allotted to them in medieval society, and partly an attempt to check extravagance. In France sumptuary laws were passed in 1563, 1565,

1567, 1572, 1577, 1590, 1591 and 1629; so many were passed because none had any effect. In England four such laws were passed, but all were ignored by the population. In 1336 Edward III made a law forbidding anyone to have more than two courses at any meal except at principal religious feasts such as Christmas or Easter. This law had no effect on behaviour, although it was not repealed until the reign of Queen Victoria. A similar statute in 1517 limited the number of courses that could be served according to the rank of the most important person present, so that nine could be served if a cardinal was present, six for a member of parliament, and three for a citizen with an income of 500 pounds a year. In 1548 Edward VI passed a law commanding all men to eat fish on religious fast days, not for religious reasons so much as to encourage the trade of fishermen. The more experienced fishermen there were, the more skilled sailors would be available for the navy in time of war.

The same motives prompted Elizabeth I in 1563 to pass a 'bill for better observance of fast days and regulating how many dishes of flesh shall be at table'. The act made it compulsory to eat fish on Wednesdays, unless one took out a special licence. It gave powers to local justices to appoint 'searchers to detect persons eating or dressing flesh on fast days' and the Fishmongers' Company had the power to check that butchers complied. These laws were almost impossible to enforce and were widely flouted.

Today in parts of North Africa the eating of dogs (cynophagy) is forbidden by law, but dog meat is regarded as such a delicacy that the habit continues covertly. This also occurs in Hong Kong where cynophagy is illegal but dog meat is particularly favoured in the Chinese cuisine. The carcasses of dogs are openly on sale in markets. In Russia during the nineteenth century a series of famines had a catastrophic effect because the peasants depended on grain as their single major food. The government responded by trying to encourage the peasants to grow and eat potatoes, a vegetable rarely used in Russia at that time. In 1840 a government decree ordered state peasants to plant a quota of potatoes on common land. Even the priesthood was called upon to aid this campaign to introduce the potato. There was widespread opposition to this policy, partly because of reluctance to move away from the traditional rye to this new uncertain crop, but partly because of fundamentalist religious objections. The 'Old Believers' regarded the potato as the devil's apple, eaten by Adam and Eve in the Garden of Eden, and said that to eat it was to disobey God's will. The conflict caused riots in ten provinces of European Russia and in Siberia, and the government eventually gave up the attempt to force the change through and retreated to a policy of persuasion. In *On Liberty* John Stuart Mill declared that: 'A person's taste is as much his own peculiar concern as his opinions or his purse.' Today's equivalent of the sumptuary laws, the exhortation by health educators to follow diets which reduce the risk of heart disease, have little effect on adults. Established food habits are hard to abandon. Unless there is direct control of the food supply, as in wartime rationing, people will resist and evade external control of their eating habits.

Your food habits tell you who you are

Food habits have very little to do with nutritional need; they have a great deal to do with other human needs such as those for love, respect, and identity. This may be one of the reasons why they are so resistant to change.

In most cultures sharing food with another person is a sign of a special relationship. The word 'companion' comes from the Latin for sharing bread, one of our staple foods; the Bantu speak about the 'clanship of porridge', linking friendship with their staple food. In China whom you eat with is a sign of your social standing, so that to eat alone is a sign of shame. Different types of eating together mark different boundaries of friendship and degrees of intimacy; there are clear differences between eating in a canteen at work with workmates, sharing drinks in a pub with acquaintances, inviting friends to one's home for dinner, and sharing Christmas lunch with close relatives. Sitting down and sharing a meal with someone is an expression of equality with them. Close-knit social groups or networks eat together; Parliament is full of convivial dining clubs that bring together separately Tory wets (the One Nation group), Tory drys (the 92 Club), and smart Tories (the Blue Chips). Oxford and, particularly, Cambridge Universities are noted for ostentatious feasts, with associated dining clubs such as Ad Eundem (which began in 1864). There are also dining clubs for public school headmasters (the 27, The Gang) and senior members of the Church of England (Nobody's Friends started in 1800). Old boy networks and new girl networks meet at mealtimes.

In times of social change eating together is usually highly symbolic. It is no accident that the Civil Rights movement for black Americans in the 1950s began with the assertion of the right of blacks to sit and eat with whites at lunch counters. Nor is it coincidental that when the Italian psychiatric hospitals were dismantled in the early 1980s by the Psychiatrica Democratica movement, one of the changes in the new mental health centres was that staff and patients should eat together. During the Middle Ages some of the new monastic orders attempted to level class distinction within monasteries by having all monks eat together. Japanese car factories in Britain have introduced canteens for all staff for much the same purpose. As will be seen in Chapter 8, eating together and sharing food are universally practised within groups of hunter gatherers such as the Australian Aborigines. Some theorists have argued that the evolutionary value to our species of sharing food led to the development of man's social co-operative nature.

The food a person eats tells us much about his identity. Real Men don't eat quiche. In the *Canterbury Tales* Geoffrey Chaucer characterised everyone by their food habits, for example the delicate taste and sensibility of the social-climbing prioress. In the same city different groups mark their separate social and religious identities by the meals they prepare. In Beirut Sunni Muslims who command coastal cities and ports are partial to fish dishes such as trabulsia (baked fish stuffed with walnuts and tahini sauce). The Shiah Muslims from southern Lebanon are strict vegetarians and likely to eat mujadara (lentils and burghul). The Druse drink maté tea from South America, and the Christian Maronites eat grilled kibbe. Culinary divisions mark off religious and cultural divisions, and are often used to insult or criticise other groups. 'Krauts', 'Limeys', 'Frogs', and 'Macaronis' are still familiar insults. The word 'eskimo' is a North American Indian word meaning 'eaters of raw flesh', meant to draw attention to what the Indians saw as a disgusting habit. (Eskimos call themselves 'Inuit', meaning 'the real people'.)

When two cultures meet for the first time they are often repelled by each other's food. When the Spaniards invaded Mexico in the sixteenth century, the Aztecs considered it possible that they might be gods. One reason for this was their traditional story that Quetzalcoatl, a bearded god, had left their land, sailing towards the rising sun, but would one day return. The arrival of these strange bearded men in ships from that very direction was therefore an extraordinary event. In order to see whether they were the returning gods, the Emperor Montezuma sent emissaries bearing food that the gods were believed to eat – turkeys, turkey eggs and white tortillas sprinkled with fresh human blood. The Spaniards were disgusted and did not eat, and the Aztecs reasoned that they were mere mortals. Truly, one culture's relish is another culture's disgust.

Foods as status symbols

What you eat shows who you are and what you are worth. Queen Victoria used to take her breakfast in the garden at Osborne in the Isle of Wight in a manner befitting one of the most powerful monarchs the world has ever known. She breakfasted under a green, fringed tent, surrounded by her

Indian servants. Every single object on her breakfast table (save her china cup and saucer) was made of solid gold. The Roman Emperor Caligula had gone further. He expressed his own position and personality by swallowing valuable pearls dissolved in vinegar, and offering guests meals of golden bread and golden meat. Prestige foods have always been used to demonstrate wealth and position. Among the Aztecs only the nobles ate roast dog. In the Middle Ages sugar was a rare, expensive prestige food. It had probably been brought to Europe as a result of contact with the Arab world, either by crusaders or through the Arab invasion of Spain. Until it was grown extensively in the New World it was expensive and beyond the reach of most people. Its main use in cookery was as a spice rather than as a sweetener: in small quantities it alters the flavour of food without sweetening. Thomas Aquinas the great medieval theologian argued that because it was a spice that eased digestion sugar was not a real food, and therefore eating it did not break one's fast.

Until about 1700, sugar was exclusively a food of the rich, and only they suffered its ill effects. A German visitor to England in the reign of Elizabeth I reported that the Queen and her courtiers had bad, often black, teeth, but that the poor had healthy teeth because sugar was beyond their reach. Not being able to afford this prestige food was good for their health. Other spices were greatly prized at that time, because of their ability to add variety to a restricted diet, and despite their lack of any nutritional value. Early exploration of the world by Europeans was motivated by the search for spices. Columbus discovered America whilst searching for them. Magellan's first circumnavigation of the world in 1519 was paid for by the spices he brought back, and Vasco Da Gama's first voyage to India in 1497 was paid for sixty times over by the ones he returned with. In the Middle Ages spices were as valuable as cocaine and heroin are today. Wealth was flaunted by the rich in sumptuous banquets. Henry IV's coronation banquet included forty-five dishes made from ingredients unavailable to his subjects. Other times and other places had their own expensive exotica to mark the tables of the rich; in China it was bears' paws or soup made of shark fins or birds' nests. It is ironic that, apart from such rare foods as truffles and caviare, modern Western prestige foods, such as those served in Cuisine Minceur, are characterised by small portions and lack of richness.

Eating as bravery

The motives for eating one particular type of food, the Japanese fugu fish, are a complex mixture of pleasure, bravery, foolhardiness, and sensation-seeking. As the Japanese poet wrote:

> Those who eat fugu soup are stupid
> but those who don't eat fugu soup are also stupid.

The fugu is a variety of puffer fish – so called because, when alarmed, it can puff itself up into a ball two or three times its normal size. In Japan it is prized for its taste, but has the unfortunate drawback of containing a virulent poison – tetrodotoxin (TTX), which is 300 times more powerful than cyanide. Nearly two-thirds of cases of fugu poisoning end in rapid paralysis and death. The poison is concentrated in the ovaries, intestines and liver of the fish, and skilled chefs are licensed to prepare fugu in restaurants; it is served up in tiny portions of thinly sliced flesh, artistically arranged on the plate. Gourmets are still drawn to the liver of the fish despite, or because of, the danger involved. In 1975 a noted Kabuki performer, Mitsugoro Bando VIII, who had been declared a 'living national treasure' by the Japanese government, died after eating four portions of fugu liver. Every year twenty or so Japanese die after eating fugu, although many others survive the enjoyment of eating this expensive delicacy. The ambivalence towards this fish is summed up by the line of a poem:

> I am dying to eat fugu, but I don't want to die.

The desire to eat fugu has nothing to do with nutrition, little to do with taste, and much to do with more profound motives.

The toxin of the fugu found its own peculiar place in literary history in the James Bond novel *From Russia with Love*, when the book ends with the hero succumbing to TTX. This enters his body not through the pleasure of eating fugu but through the painful experience of being stabbed by a poisoned blade in the boot of the Russian agent Rosa Kleb. (Only in the next novel, *Dr No*, did the world discover that the dose was not fatal.) TTX has also been claimed as the means by which voodoo witch doctors in Haiti enslave zombies. The suggestion is that a non-lethal dose of the toxin is used to induce a period of paralysis which simulates death, rather like what happens to Juliet in *Romeo and Juliet*. When the paralysed (rather than dead) are later raised up by the witch doctor they are in fact alive but confused, the 'living confused' rather than the 'living dead'.

Eating dangerous foods is not peculiar to the Japanese. Lampreys, eels traditionally regarded as a delicacy in England, contain the poison ptomaine, and an excess of this was responsible for the deaths of Henry I in 1135 and Alexander Pope in 1744.

Food sayings

We can see the importance of taste and food in our lives when we look at the expressions we use. Eating is a central part of life and provides material and metaphors for the way we think. What other human activity supplies us with so many phrases and expressions?

When you realise what's eating you, you can chew it over, or just let it stew. You could waffle on about your beef while chewing the fat with your sweetheart, or just make a corny joke. If your humour were an acquired taste rather than the spice of life, and you got a sour look, a bland expression, or raspberry in reply you could get cheesed off. If your friend thought this was just a load of boloney and that you were a bad egg a bitter feeling could make you realise that you were just eating up time. The apple of your eye thought that you were just trying to curry favour or butter them up; no longer flavour of the month, you would have to be cool as a cucumber or end up eating humble pie. You could eat your heart out, or as salt of the earth, ham it up; the bittersweet feelings might make you feel as keen as mustard and show that you had the proof of the pudding when it came to bread and butter issues.

Conclusion

Our food habits become as much a part of our mental being as the food we eat becomes a part of our physical being. As we look at our eating habits we look into every corner of our lives.

2

Do we want what we need?

We cannot choose to like one food or to dislike another; our preferences have little to do with rational choice. What, then, does affect them? An answer that many people put forward is 'instinct'. We 'instinctively' like the food which our body requires, just as a swallow instinctively flies off to Africa in the winter. Instinct is supposed to make us want what we need.

Do we 'know' what we need?

Can we rely on instinct to guide our appetite to choose what our body needs? Can we put our feelings about food on autopilot? The idea that we can, because we naturally or instinctively want what we need, has been expressed by many people over the centuries. Two hundred years ago the French philosopher Jean-Jacques Rousseau persuasively argued that, given the opportunity, humans will eat what they need and no more. 'Our appetite is only excessive because we try to impose on it rules other than those of nature, opposing, controlling, prescribing, adding, or subtracting; the scales are always in our hands, but the scales are the measure of our caprices, not of our stomachs.' Was Rousseau right? Since his time scientists have discovered that many processes within the human body are instinctive and can be left on autopilot, without our needing to understand them or to interfere. The temperature of the body is kept at almost the same level regardless of the temperature around us, without the need for us to pay any attention to it (except in extreme conditions). Is our appetite the same? Today we hear Rousseau's message from experts on eating disorders (such as 'compulsive eating') who claim that too much conscious concern about dieting distorts and swamps natural controls on appetite. Therefore, they argue, sufferers need to 'get back in touch with their bodies' so as to allow their natural appetites to reassert themselves. If your body tells you that it needs chocolate, then you should have as much chocolate as you want. Are they correct when they say we should follow our feelings, and be confident in our instincts?

The 'salt boy'

There are several dramatic examples that appear to show that we do have the ability to want what we need. There are rare cases of unfortunate children, born with metabolic defects which distort their needs for food. In one case a boy was born with a medical problem (an abnormal adrenal system) which made him permanently short of sodium, which is present in salt. His life was endangered by this problem, although no one was aware of it at the time. From about one year of age he started licking salt off crackers, and gesturing that he wanted more. When provided with bacon he would lick off the salt and then spit the meat out. His parents tried to tempt him with many foods but he disliked them and ate very little. Then one day they sprinkled some salt on to his food and it was very clear how strongly he liked it. His parents described how they learned of his need for salt.

This was the beginning of his showing that he really craved salt, because this one time was all it took for him to learn what was in the shaker. For a few days after that, when I would feed him his dinner . . . he would keep crying for something that wasn't on the table and always pointed to the cupboard . . . I held him up in front of the cupboard to see what he wanted. He picked out the salt at once . . . and I let him have it. He poured some out and ate it by dipping his finger in it. After this he would not eat any food without having the salt, too.

Following this discovery the boy refused to eat foods which were not salty, or to which salt had not been added. The need for salt played such a large part in his life that 'salt' was one of the first words he said. His behaviour is a clear illustration that, under some circumstances, human nutritional requirements can direct food preferences. He instinctively knew what he wanted. But the circumstances here were extraordinary, and the need for salt so desperate as to threaten the child's life; the search for salt may have been no more surprising than the search for water by someone deprived of fluid for days. The most interesting question to answer is whether normal children under normal circumstances show the capacity to regulate their own food choices; do normal children display instinctive 'nutritional wisdom'?

Self-service for babies

An imaginative attempt to answer this question was carried out in Chicago in the 1920s by a paediatrician called Clara Davis. She brought up fifteen infants on a 'self-service' diet, allowing them to choose what they ate for six months or more at a time. She argued that if infants do want what they need they should instinctively select a healthy diet for themselves. She brought the children into hospital while they were still being breastfed by their mothers; they had never eaten any kind of solid food before. After a few days in the hospital the mother left and the child began on the 'self-service' diet. At each mealtime the child sat down alone in a quiet room with a tray covered with dishes of different foods. A nurse was present, but she did not offer food or react to what the child ate. If the child reached for or gestured towards a dish the nurse was allowed to take up a spoonful; if he opened his mouth for it she she was allowed to feed it to him. The child, not the nurse, decided what the child ate. The babies were allowed to eat as they wished, with their hands if necessary, and when they had obviously finished eating, the tray was taken away. The aim of the study was for the children to choose for themselves everything they ate over a period of six months or longer.

A wide variety of foods (listed in Table 2) was available at each mealtime. Each type of food, even salt, was served in a separate dish on the tray; no food was salted, nor was milk added to cereal. If the child ever finished a whole serving of a particular food, the portion size was increased on the next occasion; it was assumed that if the child did not eat all of the serving of a particular food the portion size was sufficient.

What were the results? The children thrived on the 'self-service' regime, and developed as well as any other children.

Table 2   Food provided as part of the 'Self-service' diet study

Meats beef+, lamb*, chicken*	*Eggs* +
Offal liver*, kidneys*, brains*, sweetbreads*	*Milk*
	Fruits apples oranges bananas tomatoes peaches pineapple
Fish haddock	
	Vegetables lettuce, cabbage+, spinach, cauliflower, peas+, beets, carrots+, turnips, potatoes
Cereals ground whole wheat+, oatmeal+, barley, corn meal, rye	*Bone products* bone marrow+, bone jelly
Sea salt	

All meats, vegetables, and fruits were finely cut, mashed, or ground; those marked * were cooked: those marked + were served both raw and cooked

They enjoyed their food, showed healthy appetites, and were free from diarrhoea, constipation, and any digestive disorder. The food that they chose to eat over a six-month period was nutritionally adequate and balanced, and provided at least as good a diet as the hospital food served to other children. However, this sufficient balanced diet was achieved by unconventional means which Davis described as 'a dietitian's nightmare'.

During the first few weeks on the regime the infants tasted all the foods, almost at random, swallowing some and spitting out others. Gradually, as the days went by, they became able to recognise particular foods and made clear choices, tending to eat about three solid foodstuffs during each meal. Although the diet was balanced in the long term it was not balanced in the short term, at each meal. Some of the meals chosen, such as a breakfast of a pint of orange juice and some liver, or a supper of eggs, banana and milk, did not conform to what was normally thought of as 'proper children's meals'. They showed some lasting likes and dislikes but also striking temporary preferences, just as if they had series of cravings for particular foods lasting for weeks at a time. Davis could find no clear reason for this phenomenon, but speculated that these waves of cravings might reflect the changing nutritional needs of the growing infant.

Several interesting events suggested that the children showed 'dietary wisdom' by wanting what they needed. They all regularly ate salt – despite disliking it and coughing, spluttering, and crying when they did taste it. Salt is the most accessible form of sodium which is essential for health. This is sometimes forgotten today when, with a more adequate diet, there is much concern about the harmful consequences of excessive salt intake such as high blood pressure.

One of the boys entered the study suffering from rickets, for which cod-liver oil was the usual remedy. A container of this, and one of milk to which it was added was always placed on his tray. He drank these regularly during the first three months and then stopped abruptly, drinking no more. Regular tests showed that the rickets had healed by this time. It was as though he had an appetite for cod-liver oil while his body needed it. These and other examples have been interpreted as showing that humans do have a measure of 'nutritional wisdom' and that if we can 'listen to our bodies' we will eat what is good for us.

It is difficult to draw such confident conclusions from the results of this study, for several reasons. The first is that those caring for the children were aware of the purpose of the study and may have inadvertently influenced the children's choices. The nurses were asked to present the tray of food impassively, but they knew which foods were supposed to be nutritious and may have unintentionally influenced the children in subtle ways through smiles, hesitations, sighs, or other non-verbal signals. We cannot rule out this possibility. The second difficulty lies in the nature of the foods presented to the children. As Table 2 shows, these tended to be unprocessed foods often rich in fibre; even choices made at random among these should lead to a reasonably healthy diet. It would be much more impressive if the same results occurred when the children were also offered sweet or highly processed foods.

Studies of individual cases such as the 'salt boy', and of Clara Davis's self-service diet for babies suggest that sometimes we instinctively do choose to eat what our body requires. In adults the question is whether we can balance our energy needs and energy intake, and whether our spontaneous urges, cravings, and dislikes of foods are indications of the body's needs.

Rats do it . . .

Studies of this issue have tended to focus on our intake of energy, looking at whether we can adjust our food intake to our energy requirements. A major reason for this is its relevance to the problem of obesity. Obese people, by definition, have too much energy stored as fat, and as we shall see in Chapter 9, the reason why some people develop in this way is not clear. If there is some means by which most people regulate their energy intake, then maybe these controls are defective in obese people. Another reason for the interest in energy is that some species, such as rats, show very precise control over their energy intake. In some sense they 'know' how much energy to take in and vary the amount they eat according to the energy content of the food. If the calorie content of each gramme of their food is doubled, they eat only half as much; if it is halved, they eat twice as much. Only in extraordinary conditions does this system break down. With this example and concerns about obesity in mind, it is interesting to see whether humans can also regulate their energy intake.

Six-week-old babies do it . . .

Young infants have been studied because of the simplicity of their diet – milk – and because they have had little learning experience which might complicate or mask any regulatory mechanisms. In the late 1970s an American paediatrician, Samuel Fomon, conducted studies on infants who were bottle-fed. He tried to see whether they were like rats, and would drink more if their milk had less energy in it, and less if it had more energy in it. He compared how much milk young babies drank when it was either the usual kind (67 calories per 100 ml), or richer in energy (133 calories) or lower in energy (53 calories). The researchers provided the mothers with bottles of the ready-made-up milk; the bottles were weighed carefully before and after each feed. It was then possible to look at the effects of varying the energy content of the milk provided.

They found that younger babies showed few signs of regulating their energy intake; if they were provided with a calorie-rich milk, they drank just as much of it and so took in more energy and put on more weight. The pattern changed once babies reached about six weeks of age; those fed a more concentrated milk started drinking less, so that their energy intake was the same as that of the others. Similarly, babies fed the more diluted milk started to drink more of it (to compensate for the lack of energy) when they reached six weeks or so. It was as though babies have a regulatory mechanism which takes this time to develop or mature.

Sometimes adults can do it . . .

Can adults do what babies can at six weeks of age? The first studies of this contrived a situation rather like breastfeeding, a 'food dispensing machine' which pumps liquid foods directly into the subject's mouth through a steel straw. Whenever someone wants to eat, he presses a button and liquid is pumped up into his mouth. The container of food is hidden from the subjects so that they cannot consciously keep track of how much they have eaten; in this sense, feeding from this machine is like breastfeeding. Adults took part in experiments just like Fomon's studies with babies. For three weeks volunteers carried on their normal lives as far as possible, but took all their food from the machine (apart from water, black coffee, and tea). During the first week the liquid food (a flavoured milky drink) was consistent in its energy content; then for the next 10 days the energy value was halved, though the food tasted the same. The subjects in the experiment did not know that this had happened, and the question was whether they would respond to the change. If they were able to regulate their energy intake they would compensate by drinking twice as much of the more diluted food, just as the babies did.

In fact what was found was that people vary tremendously. Some failed to show any degree of compensation but carried on consuming the same quantity of food, and lost weight steadily. Others gradually increased their intake over a few days on the new, diluted, food and stayed at the same weight. No one drank sufficient of the diluted food to compensate completely. The predominant pattern was a sluggish incomplete compensation – a much more poorer performance than that given by the rats who, under similar circumstances, showed themselves much more finely tuned. The result of this study showed that there was a certain amount of adjustment over several days, but that it was usually incomplete. There were no differences between obese and non-obese persons in this.

What about real food?

Eating liquid food from a machine is highly artificial; liquid food is very different from what people usually eat. How far do these conclusions apply to 'normal' meals composed of solid foods? The difficulty, until recently, has been in reducing the energy of foods without altering their taste noticeably. In order to test whether compensatory eating occurs it is essential that the food that is low in energy does not differ in any other way from normal food, and that the two types cannot be distinguished. Recently this has been made possible with the development of aspartame, an artificial energy-free sweetener with a much more natural taste than saccharin. It tastes so much more like sugar than saccharin that it has largely replaced it in low-energy slimming products. When the change-over occurred, some slimmers had got so used to the distinctive taste of saccharin that they interpreted the change in flavour as a signal that products such as soft drinks were no longer low-calorie, and complained to manufacturers about it.

Aspartame was employed in several studies with 'real food' by the American researcher Katherine Porikos. Volunteers lived in a research ward for three weeks or more, in the belief that they were taking part in a study into how the body absorbed a new drug. They chose what to eat at mealtimes from an attractive selection of foods before them; the menu included most conventional foods. They could also choose what they wanted from a refrigerator full of snacks and beverages. During the first few days foods such as ice cream, soft drinks, puddings, jam etc. were sweetened with sugar; then they were sweetened with aspartame for a fixed number of days. All the subjects' food choices were observed and, without their knowledge, all dishes were weighed before and after meals. The results were clear. When the reduced-energy foods were substituted the volunteers carried on eating the same sorts of foods as before but failed to eat sufficient to compensate fully for the missing calories. Once sugar had been eliminated they ate enough to compensate for only half of the missing calories.

The same pattern – of incomplete and sluggish regulation – was observed for both solid and liquid foods, and in neither case were there any marked differences between obese and non-obese persons. This shows that our desire for foods is only partly determined by our energy needs. It also suggests that obesity is not caused by a lack of responsiveness to energy needs. Adult humans are certainly not as good at balancing their energy intake as babies, four-year-olds, or indeed, rats. The result of this test also has the practical implication that the reduced-energy foods for slimmers (which are like the aspartame-sweetened foods in the previous experiment) are a worthwhile dieting aid. If perfect energy regulation did occur we would completely compensate for the reduction in energy by eating more, so as to take in the same amount of energy; the fact that compensation is incomplete provides the food industry with a challenging opportunity to produce reduced energy foods for slimmers which are hard to distinguish from 'normal' foods.

Urges and cravings

Many people experience urges and cravings for particular foods, or even for substances which aren't usually thought of as foods. Does this mean that they actually need to eat these? Is it the body telling them what they need? Are they like the boy who craved salt because his body needed it? Are these examples of 'wanting what we need'? There are two main types of urges and cravings, those which occur in pregnancy and those which occur at other times and are for non-foods such as earth (geophagy), or ice (pagophagy). This second type of craving is called pica, after the Latin word for magpie.

Cravings and aversions during pregnancy

Pregnant women commonly experience changes in their appetite. The three most frequent types of change are sickness and nausea in the early stages of pregnancy, cravings to eat particular foods or substances, and intense aversions or dislikes of foods that are usually eaten.

Nausea and vomiting occur frequently in about eighty per cent of pregnancies, particularly during the first three months (the first trimester). These symptoms do not occur in any other species and no one has ever been able to clearly establish their cause. Many people have suggested that changes in hormone levels may be involved, but these changes also occur in other mammals that do not experience nausea during pregnancy. The absence of nausea is associated with a higher risk of foetal death; the reason for this is also unknown. Because the first trimester is the time when the developing foetus is most at risk, vomiting may well have some protective function. Whether or not a pregnant woman will experience nausea and vomiting is affected by her attitude to the pregnancy; some observers have found that women who reject the child (and especially those seeking abortions) are much less likely to vomit. Cultural and social factors are probably also important; in South Africa vomiting is five times as common among blacks as among whites. Although at first it might seem that nausea has a purely physical cause, it is clear that psychological and social factors are important. Our ignorance about this is enormous.

Cravings and aversions are strong desires for foods that are not usually eaten and repulsion of foods that normally are eaten, and they often occur in pregnancy. They are not the result of some rational process of thought (like deciding to drink less alcohol in order not to harm the foetus) but occur spontaneously, even against one's will (like finding that one cannot drink alcohol even though one wants to). Historical accounts record a wide variety of foods and other substances, including coal, sand, eels and frogs, that pregnant women have craved. Surveys show that over half of pregnant women in Western countries experience cravings, and that these are most commonly directed towards fruit and fruit drinks, and then towards sweet-tasting foods such as ice cream and chocolate. Strong-tasting foods, such as pickles, or chewy foods such as nuts, are also commonly craved. Do these cravings express a need for high energy (i.e. sweet) foods during a time when the foetus is growing rapidly? The energy required for pregnancy is about 80,000 calories, and for lactation about 2,750 calories per day; there are increased needs for minerals such as iron and calcium. Pregnancies require energy and sweet foods provide it. Or do cravings result from a blunting of the senses of taste and smell during pregnancy? There is some evidence that taste becomes less sensitive with pregnancy and reverts to normal within a few hours of the birth. This change is particularly striking in the case of salt – pregnant women have a much less sensitive palate for salty tastes than women who are not pregnant but recover their sensitivity soon after delivery. Pregnant women also have a much greater liking for stronger salty tastes, which may reflect the greater need for salt during pregnancy. This could explain why cravings are so often directed towards foods such as oranges and pickles, which have very strong and distinctive tastes. Chewy foods might be more attractive if taste is dulled.

Aversions in pregnancy are rarely directed towards the types of food that satisfy cravings, but are most often focused on protein foods (such as meat or fish), and then on beverages (such as tea, coffee, or alcohol), and fried or greasy food. Aversions tend to start earlier in pregnancy than cravings, and to persist longer. On average aversions manifest themselves in the first twelve weeks, but cravings can begin at any time. Few aversions last beyond the end of pregnancy. Many aversions are acquired by conditioning processes, unconsciously associating the food with the nausea that followed it (this kind of conditioning is discussed in detail in Chapter 4). This explains why most begin during the first trimester, when nausea is most frequent, and why most are directed towards protein foods, just as other taste aversions are. Not all aversions are acquired through conditioning, and the tendency to develop aversions at that time may help to protect the foetus when it is at its most vulnerable to toxins, which is in the first trimester.

One of the most interesting findings about cravings and aversions is that they tend to occur together (so that women who experience one are likely to experience the other) and that they both occur more frequently in women who have other 'oral' habits such as smoking, drinking, or eating under stress. As we shall see in Chapter 8, Sigmund Freud, the founder of psychoanalysis, suggested that because of events early in life, some people have 'oral fixations' and tend to develop a range of habits which involve putting things into their mouths. The evidence suggests that 'oral' women are most likely to develop cravings and aversions.

The changes in diet caused by nausea, cravings and aversions during pregnancy do not seem to be related to specific nutritional needs, and so do not provide good examples of 'knowing what we need'. They are influenced by cultural and psychological factors as much as physical ones.

Pica

Pica is the craving to eat substances which are not foods and which have no nutritional value; examples include coal, faeces, soap, insects, and petrol. Pica is not a habit confined to pregnancy alone and occurs less commonly in pregnancy than aversion. Far from being merely individual fancies, some forms of pica (especially geophagy – eating earth) have been normal behaviour in nations as far apart as Peru, China and India. In ancient Greece dried clay from the island of Lemnos was sold to be eaten, and many Greeks believed that eating clay helped young men to acquire the slender rather feminine type of body that they so admired. Today in areas of Africa eating earth during the first trimester of pregnancy is believed to prevent nausea, and tablets of clay are sold in markets to be eaten. Varieties of clay are mined from different locations for their particular properties; those from certain sites, such as termite mounds (which tend to be rich in minerals), are particularly favoured. Clay is used as medicine for a range of disorders including diarrhoea and intestinal parasitic diseases like hookworm. In West African countries, such as Ghana, clay is consumed by pregnant or lactating women as a nutritional supplement, much as British women might take iron tablets or vitamin tablets. One survey in West Africa found that half the women regularly ate clay, the average daily consumption being 30 g (1 oz). Chemical analyses of pieces of clay sold for this use revealed that they contain sufficient quantities of iron, copper and calcium to be a useful supplement, especially where nutrition is inadequate, and are a cheap, easily available counterpart to Western pharmaceutical preparations.

Geophagy crossed the Atlantic with West Africans abducted to a life of slavery in North America, and still survives today among black Americans in the Southern states. Geophagy amongst pregnant women in the South was estimated at fifty-five per cent in 1957; by 1974 it had fallen to eighteen per cent. It was widely practised by both adults and children in rural black communities during the first half of this century but has become less common with each decade. As cotton plantations grew and proliferated the black slave population was dispersed. Yet the earth of home, which had been eaten in childhood, was often preferred and sought after and the custom grew of sending containers of earth to those who had moved away. Even today clay is sold in markets in the South, and boxes of clay are given as presents to pregnant women. This custom is often supported by superstitious beliefs, such as that it will prevent the new-born baby being marked at birth. People who move away from an area in early adulthood often request 'childhood' clay to be sent to them or return to dig their own. The 'return to the country' to dig up clay occurs in a similar form among other first generation urban dwellers who retain links with their roots, e.g. Irish city dwellers who return 'home' to cut peat turf from the family plot. Where the earth of home is not easily accessible in the Northern States laundry starch has often been eaten (amylophphagy) as a substitute. This has none of the nutritional advantages of clay, although it can be made into a mud-like consistency, and contains more energy. Another substitute is ice; eating large quantities of this (pagophagy), in the region of 1½ lbs per day, is practised particularly, but not only, by pregnant women.

Surveys in Britain have found relatively few cases of pica, even during pregnancy. In 1957 a BBC radio programme on the subject asked listeners to write in with their experiences. From these accounts the substances most craved were (in descending order of importance) coal, soap, disinfectant, toothpaste, mothballs and petrol. Most of these have strong and distinctive tastes or smells, and their choice may be related to changes in these senses during pregnancy. There were no cultural traditions to guide preferences, as with the American blacks.

Not surprisingly pica can have harmful side-effects ranging from obstructing or perforating the intestines, introducing parasitic infection, and even death. It can also cause anaemia or other deficiencies by reducing the intake of nutritious foods or by interfering with the body's capacity to extract minerals from foods.

Pica in animals is usually related to some dietary deficiency, so that, for example, cattle deficient in phosphorus have been observed to eat bones. In such cases correcting the deficiency abolishes pica. In Australia sheep eating a variety of objects were found to be deficient in copper. Their pica vanished when they were given a copper supplement. In humans there is also a strong link between pica and nutritional deficiencies, especially of iron. Pica has often (but not always) been found to occur in anaemic adults and children, and to be cured by administering iron. But pica cannot always be explained as compensation for deficiency, because only a minority of anaemic individuals eat earth or other non-food substances, and those who do do not always eat substances which are particularly rich in iron. Eating ice is also associated with anaemia and reversed by iron tablets, although ice does not contain iron. These groups of habits represent the joint action of biological and social forces. Within certain subcultures eating earth is acceptable behaviour, but not everyone does it; those who do it and who are in need of minerals within the earth learn the benefits of this habit from experience.

What we know about urges and cravings does not support the view that these are the direct expression of some bodily need, and that we should follow them with confidence. Cravings by pregnant women for sweet or tasty foods are rarely directed towards those foods which are available and would best supply their needs; they may be better explained by changes in the sense of taste. The habit of eating earth may have begun in Africa out of experiences with clay and represent a beneficial dietary supplement in a poorly fed population. It was part of the culture transported to North America by the slaves; in that new environment it has remained part of the culture, but has been distorted and continues in forms where it is no longer of any biological significance.

So, do we want what we need?

To some degree we do want what we need; this shows up most clearly in experiments that allow us to examine processes like energy regulation. But in everyday life this 'instinctive' capacity is swamped by other forms of learning and experience. We have an autopilot, but it easily gets confused, and its mechanism gets overridden and jammed.

It is also misleading to think about this capacity as an 'instinct' that we are born with, just as the swallow is born with the instinct to fly south in the winter. The examples of the 'salt boy' and the children on the self-service diet show that they learned to like what they needed; they were not born with the information. The 'salt boy' didn't know that he needed salt: he only discovered this from his experience of eating it. The children on the self-service diet started by trying to eat everything (even the plate in some cases!). Their likes and dislikes developed out of their experiences with food; they learned to like what they needed. The most important instinct that we are born with is the capacity to learn from our experience. The success of our species lies in its adaptability; unlike all other species Homo sapiens flourishes in every environment on earth and has a unique ability to learn and adapt. We learn from our experiences with food, and sometimes we learn to want what we need. At other times this capacity is swamped, just as Rousseau suggested it could be.

In the next chapters we look at how we learn to like and dislike foods from conception onwards so that we can understand why we sometimes want what we need and sometimes want what we certainly do not need.

3

Learning what to like: how children develop food preferences

Humans are born helpless, totally dependent on adults for their food and survival; during the first few months of life they can consume only one very bland type of food: milk. Once babies start eating solids their food world expands dramatically; the variety of potential textures and flavours of food increases considerably, even though the foods that a baby can sample are limited to what adults offer it. As the young child begins to move independently of its parents, first by crawling, and then by walking, it becomes able to seek out foods for itself. The baby extends its range of food experiences until, in childhood, it eats almost the same range of foods as adults. Children take for granted which things are food and which are not, despite the arbitrariness of this. How does the child learn one 'language' of food, thus excluding others? What factors are involved in this process and can likes and dislikes be unlearned?

Learning before birth?

We experience taste long before our birth. The taste buds and other parts of the taste system are formed and operating by the twelfth week after conception. The growing foetus shows swallowing movement from about the same time and can sense the taste of the amniotic fluid in which it rests. The taste of this fluid varies markedly, and is influenced by, for example, urination by the foetus. It is also affected by the mother's diet. The foetus is exposed to the taste of the mother's diet for six months before birth, and may become familiar with certain tastes during that time. Experiments carried out with rats have established that such prenatal learning can occur. In one study pregnant rats regularly drank alcohol with their water; their pups showed a greater liking for alcohol than other rats did, even when they were adults and had never tasted alcohol since birth. It would be obviously unacceptable to carry out the same sort of experiments with humans, and so we cannot definitely prove that our experiences before birth affect our food preferences. However, it is very likely that this does occur, and that by the time of its birth the baby has already developed some preferences from experience. This is particularly interesting since, before birth, taste has no connection with feeding.

Preferences present at birth

Two great changes occur in human feeding at birth. The mouth is used for feeding for the first time and the baby takes an active part in feeding. Until birth the needs of the growing foetus are supplied by the bloodstream of the mother, via the umbilical cord. The diet of the foetus is directly determined by the diet of the mother (although, if the mother's diet is deficient in minerals, such as calcium, the foetus can take them from the mother's body). At birth, for the first time, nutrition becomes linked to the mouth, and to taste. From birth onwards feeding becomes an active process, in which the infant, totally dependent on adults for the supply of food, can choose to reject or accept food. The new-born infant possesses a complete set of taste buds and can differentiate between the major taste qualities of sweet, sour, bitter, and salty. The sense of taste is fully formed and changes little for the rest of life. From the first few breaths of life the infant shows marked preferences for sweet tastes as against sour, salty and bitter tastes. These preferences can clearly be detected from the child's facial expression, and some researchers have claimed to be able to detect four different expressions, corresponding to the four taste types. Adult expressions to the same sensations are similar and form the basis of describing the moods of others – 'he's sour', 'she's feeling bitter' etc. The relatively primitive senses of taste and smell provide the clearest metaphors for emotions and moods. Smell is different from taste because although new-born infants can appreciate different smells, they have no clear inborn likes or dislikes.

Sweetness makes the heart beat faster

A wide variety of sophisticated means has been used to investigate the capacities and preferences of the new-born; these demonstrate more subtle reactions than facial expressions to taste experiences. The young infant's heart rate increases with the pleasure of sweet tastes; sweetness makes the heart beat faster, even for very weak sweet tastes that do not affect the infant's expression. Salty fluid tends to slow down the heart rate. Although the new-born child drinks more of the sweet fluid that it likes, it is unable to stop itself drinking the salty fluid that it dislikes. Sucking and swallowing are easier to turn on than off. This is a significant practical issue, which may account for episodes of accidental salt poisoning of infants that sometimes prove fatal. Salt and sugar are both white crystalline substances, and are similar in most respects apart from their taste and their effects on bodily functioning. Sour and bitter tastes are clearly rejected by babies and probably this represents a primitive defence against harmful acids, which are almost all sour, and many naturally occurring poisons, which taste bitter. But why should new-born humans like sweet things? This preference is also found in all other mammals, so there must be a reason for it – what is it?

Sweet foods that occur in nature are relatively high in energy and so a liking for sweet foods leads creatures to increase their energy intake. The most important task of new-born mammals is to grow, and they require energy to do this; nearly half of the energy intake of a human infant is used for growth, a higher proportion than ever again in its life (at no other time in our lives do we double our weight in a few months!). Milk is also sweet, and so the taste preferences present at birth in all mammals make their mother's milk attractive to them.

Mere familiarity is enough

One way in which preferences for foods are formed is by experience – the more experience we have of tasting something, the better we like it. This applies to adults as well as children, and to many things other than foods, for example music, paintings, and faces. (This is rather humbling, we like to think that we prefer the music of Mozart or Chopin because of our good judgement rather than because we have often been exposed to it and it has 'grown' on us.) This principle was first clearly formulated by Robert Zajonc, an American psychologist, in 1968. He argued that greater familiarity leads to greater liking, however that familiarity is caused, so that 'mere exposure' can affect preferences. There is strong evidence that 'mere exposure' affects the food preferences of humans and other mammals.

Learning at the mother's breast

The infant who consumes only milk is passively exposed to its flavour. The flavour of breast milk is not so consistent and unvarying as that of pasteurised cows' milk or milk made up from milk powder. Its taste reflects the mother's recent diet. If the mother eats fish, curry or garlic, then her milk will take on that flavour, and her baby will be exposed to it. Exposure leads to liking, and so this is one way in which the mother's food preferences help to form those of her child. Absorbing information about foodstuffs 'with mother's milk' makes these flavours familiar from the first days outside the womb. With exposure comes preference, and the more exposure the deeper and longer lasting is the preference. This has been established clearly by experiments carried out on other species, in which the diet of the lactating mother has been varied with the view to examining the effects of this on the young later in life. For instance the pups of female rats fed an onion-flavoured diet during the weeks of breastfeeding show greater preferences for onion-tasting foods when they reach adulthood, even if they have never eaten onion-tasting solid food themselves. The same effects have been shown for sugar, garlic, and even for alcohol. For obvious ethical reasons the same sorts of experiments cannot be carried out on human infants, but there is strong circumstantial evidence that exposure influences them in the same way.

A sweet drink keeps a sweet tooth

One of the most important tastes for human babies is sweetness. We are born liking sweet things; does 'mere exposure' affect this? Researchers from the Monell Chemical Senses Center in Pennsylvania examined the taste preferences of new-born infants (within two days of birth) and then tested them again six months later, and two years later. Both at birth and at follow-up there was a general preference for sugar; however, the strength of this at follow-up was influenced by the child's diet. A quarter of the children had from birth been regularly fed with water sweetened with either sugar or honey, and these had a much stronger liking for sugar at six months and at two years. Those children who had not been fed sweetened water showed a decline in their liking for sweet tastes; those who had been fed it maintained the preference seen at birth. One of the most interesting findings of this study was that drinking sweetened water only had this effect on preferences if it was given to the baby within the first six months of life. This shows that a 'sweet tooth' is inborn, but can be modified by early experience.

Introduction to solid foods

With weaning comes a transition second only to birth as a change in feeding habits; instead of consuming only one, relatively homogeneous, liquid food the child enters a more complex food world with increasing variety of flavour and texture. In most societies newly weaned children are not immediately exposed to the full repertoire of adult meals, but eat a limited range of 'children's foods'. Societies that add spices, such as chilli pepper, to all adult foods keep them out of children's food. Even so there are marked differences between cultures in how rapidly children are introduced to adult foods. Even two such similar nations as Britain and France differ noticeably from one another; in France a wide variety of dishes is presented to children at an age when British children are still eating bland mush. The introduction to solid food is an important part of the initiation into a culture. This is seen in such symbolic acts as the presentation of salt as part of Christian baptism, or the ceremony of the Gadsup people of New Guinea in which the father's brother places food on the infant's tongue with these words: 'We give you these foods from our gardens so that you will want these foods and work hard to grow them.'

Learning through experience; familiarity overcomes neophobia

The young child starting to eat solid foods is becoming less dependent on adults. With weaning comes the end of absolute dependence on adult caretakers and the beginning of the process of learning about food. Learning comes from experience and the young child can learn most from sampling a wide variety of foods, to lay the foundations of a healthy diet. In order to permit this learning experience, neophobia – the fear of the new – is at its lowest ever in the first year or two of life. All omnivores need to learn as rapidly as possible what is and what is not edible and nutritious. Species that eat only one type of food – e.g. the koala bear, which lives on eucalyptus leaves – still have need to learn, to distinguish between species of eucalyptus. Being specialised makes life easy when food is plentiful; but the koala bear without eucalyptus faces death. All animals with varied diets, such as the rat, cat, gorilla and chimpanzee, need to learn a great deal about what they can eat, and go through a period of minimal neophobia.

The principle of familiarity applies to solid foods just as it does to liquids, so that once a baby is weaned, familiar foods become more preferred, with a salty diet leading to a strong appetite for salt etc. A study into the likes and dislikes of three- and four-year-olds found that the two most important factors determining preferences were sweetness (a chemical characteristic of the food) and familiarity (a characteristic of the child's previous experience with that food).

Studies that show associations between, for example, a diet rich in sugar and high liking for sweet things, strongly suggest that familiarity causes increased liking, but they cannot prove this. This is because any such association that is observed can be explained in a variety of ways; for instance, it is possible that children with a greater need for energy naturally seek out sweet foods, and that their parents recognise this and feed them more of these foodstuffs. The only way of arriving at more definite conclusions is to carry out experiments in which children are at random exposed to different forms of food-stuffs.

Tasting gjetost makes you like it, even if you spit it out

A series of experimental studies by an American psychologist, Lean Birch, proved the effects of familiarity in two-year olds. Children were presented with foods that were novel to them;

one study employed five unusual cheeses, such as Norwegian gjetost, while another involved unusual fruit such as lychees. Each day for six weeks the children were given small pieces of two cheeses and asked to taste each of them; on many occasions, especially after tasting a particular cheese for the first time, the child spat it out. The crucial part of the experiment was to vary how often children were presented with each of the five cheeses over the six weeks; at random each child was presented with one cheese twenty times, another fifteen times, and the others ten times, five times and twice. Measures of the children's preferences for each cheese were made before and after the six-week tasting period. The results were very clear-cut; the more often a child had tasted a food the more it liked it. The same results were obtained when unusual fruits were used instead of cheeses.

The young are most susceptible

The results of experiments such as these are consistent with those of experiments on other species and suggest that the effects of familiarity are strong, and common to many omnivores; this is one example of the effects of our biological make-up on our food habits. There is also evidence which suggests very strongly that in many species the tastes of younger creatures are most susceptible to the effects of 'mere familiarity' and that neophobia becomes gradually stronger with maturity. This could go some way towards explaining why a new-born child can learn any 'food language' (firstly by absorbing characteristic tastes from its mother's milk, and then by exposure to foods of the cuisine when neophobia is minimal) and later reject other 'food languages' (through neophobia).

New food habits are most easily acquired by the young of the species. A celebrated example of this occurred in 1953 in a group of wild monkeys (macaques) living on Koshima, a small Japanese island. Researchers had supplied the monkeys with raw sweet potatoes for about a year. One day one of the younger monkeys, called Imo, was seen to do something that no monkey had been seen to do before; she washed a potato in fresh water in order to clean it of sand. She continued doing this and other monkeys started to copy her; the habit gradually spread through the colony over a period of months. It was striking that the new habit was first taken up by the younger monkeys and only later (if at all) by the adults. The same pattern was seen several years later when another monkey began dipping potatoes in sea water, presumably for the salty taste. Soon fifty per cent of young monkeys were washing their potatoes in the sea, but only ten per cent of old monkeys did this. Interestingly enough, these figures are almost the same as those recorded in the study mentioned in Chapter 1, where young immigrants to Israel brought new foods into the home which older members of their families were reluctant to accept. Taboos tend to be strongest in adults; when, after the aircrash in the Andes described in Chapter 1, survival required eating human flesh, the eldest victims of the crash delayed eating the longest, until death was imminent. Studies of the effects of exposure on the acceptance of unfamiliar foods (such as tripe) in US servicemen found that increasing familiarity had little effect with older officers; neophobia 'sets' with age.

It makes sense for there to be an early period in which food preferences can be learned easily, just as language is – young children can learn to speak several languages without any effort. Some researchers have discussed the possibility that young mammals become 'imprinted' on foods that they encounter early in life. This would not mean that subsequent learning could not occur, just that it would be more difficult; adults can learn second languages, but with more effort than is required of the young child to become bilingual.

For exposure to 'work', the unfamiliar food has to be tasted. How is this to be achieved in the first place?

Animals learn from their parents

Baby humans always eat in a social context. A young mammal

51

is born completely dependent on its parents, and only gradually, from weaning onwards, learns to feed itself, but it does this with its parents. Weaned rat pups eat novel foods more readily if their parents are already eating them. It makes biological sense for the young mammal to learn which foods to eat by copying its parents, because the very fact that they are consuming something shows that it is edible. In a world full of poisonous and non-nutritious materials, learning what is and what is not edible is an important task for the omnivore. Trial-and-error learning is too time-consuming and too risky, especially when error can result in death.

An American psychologist, Wanda Wyrwicka, showed the importance of this in some experiments with young kittens, when faced with a novel food (tuna). If they first encountered the tuna when they were with their mother, who ate the food, they explored the room freely, and then started eating the fish from the same spot on the dish as their mother ate. They began eating cautiously, keeping close to her. It took six or seven feeding sessions before they started to eat at the beginning of a session without hesitation. If, in contrast, the kittens encountered tuna for the first time when they were alone, they ignored it for much longer, and tended to 'freeze' much more; when they eventually did begin to eat they ate hesitantly, from the very edge of the dish. Having their mother present allowed them to explore the strange food much more readily. They learned from her example to accept the food, but then their increasing familiarity with it maintained its acceptability.

Wild mountain gorillas in Rwanda learn about food in much the same way. Gorillas are vegetarians and eat only leaves, fruit, stems and other parts of trees and plants. Baby gorillas spend most of their time with their mother and observe what she is eating. They stay very close to her but at the age of about five months they start picking for themselves from the plants from which she is eating, or pick up bits that she has dropped. It is very rare for them to attempt to eat anything that she is not eating. By the time that they are fully weaned (at about three or four years of age) they are eating much the same foods as their mother. No one has ever observed mother gorillas deliberately influencing the food choices of their young.

Human babies learn from adults

Social factors are crucial. The developing child is offered only a limited range of the foods that adults eat. Adults prepare and offer foods that they do not themselves eat for meals, but often demonstrate tasting them, as a means of tempting the child to eat. Ours is the only species in which parents intentionally coax and cajole their young to eat familiar foods or use a favourite foodstuff as a reward for eating a less favoured one.

The importance of adult influence was demonstrated by some Californian researchers in 1975 who examined what happened when young children were offered unfamiliar foods in their own homes. The food (e.g. a blue-coloured tortilla filled with ham and cheese) was presented either by the child's mother or by a young woman visitor, who had played happily with the child for half an hour. At random each of eighty children was offered the food 'as something to eat' either after the adults had begun to eat the food or without the adults eating. More children put the food in their mouths if it was offered by their mother (seventy-five per cent), rather than by the visitor (twenty-five per cent), and if it was offered once the adults were eating (eighty per cent) rather than if the adults didn't eat (forty-seven per cent). Younger children (fourteen to twenty months) were affected much more than older children (three-and-a-half-year-olds). The results are similar to those of the animal studies in showing the effect of seeing an adult taste a novel food. This suggests that the capacity to learn from observing others eat is part of our biological heritage.

Children affect children

As children grow older their intellect and language develop, allowing them to learn in more abstract ways and to profit from other people's experience. Children are influenced by the behaviour of other children, especially those who are slightly older than them or whom they like. Once they can think in abstract terms and can imagine fictional heroes, they can also be influenced by stories about their behaviour. This was first studied systematically in London in 1938 by the German psychologist Karl Duncker. Children attending a nursery school (aged two and a half to five years) were told a story in pairs by their teacher, and were then asked to dress up as one of the characters in it and act it out.

The story was about the plight of animals in the Big Forest in the winter when snow lay all around. A little fieldmouse, Micky, tried to eat different foods such as the bark of the hemlock tree (which tasted sour and disgusting and which he spat out). Eventually he discovered the maple tree and found that its bark tasted particularly delicious. Later on in the story Micky met his friend Eaglefeather, an Indian boy, who was hungry. Micky showed Eaglefeather how horrible the hemlock tree tasted, and he spat it out as well. Eaglefeather then sampled the delicious maple tree and cried out: 'This is really good. I love it. It's so sweet. I'll take some of it home to my people.'

One child in each pair performed the part of Eaglefeather, dressed with a feather in his or her hair, or of Micky the fieldmouse, dressed with a grey tail. On the table before them were glasses of the two novel foods described in the story, sour hemlock (actually, white chocolate adulterated with citric acid) and sweet maple sugar (actually, sugar lumps which had absorbed bitter valerian solution). While performing the story the children were asked to taste the 'hemlock' and then the 'maple' and to say which they preferred. Each child went through the process on two successive days, acting out both parts. The children who acted out the story increased their liking for the 'maple'; in contrast other children who did not know the story and were asked to taste the two 'foods' did not change their opinions about them. The results did demonstrate that social influence of this kind can exert a strong effect on food preferences, but the effect was temporary, fading away over the fortnight following the game.

Bribing children to eat foods puts them off

Children's food preferences can be influenced by brief play acting. They can be much more strongly affected by members of their family, whom they see every day. Without consciously intending to, parents (and brothers and sisters, grandparents etc.) teach their children about food and establish likes and dislikes. Paradoxically, difficulties can develop if adults consciously attempt to influence their children's preferences. Quite frequently parents try to encourage young children to eat all of some particular food (such as vegetables) by making the arrival of another more favoured food (such as ice cream) dependent on their finishing the first. What is the long-term effect of this approach, which is peculiar to our own species? Some might argue that because the child is rewarded for eating the disliked food, it will come to like it in time.

Lean Birch demonstrated that the opposite occurs. She carried out two studies in which children in a nursery school were provided with a novel milk drink (e.g. prune-flavoured milk) as a substitute for their normal drink. While they were drinking it some children were told that they would receive a treat (such as seeing a short children's film) as a reward for doing this. Other children (the control group) later received the same treat but were not told that this was connected with the drink. The procedure was repeated eight times over four weeks, and preferences for the drinks were assessed before and after this four-week period. The results were clear. Children who were not told that the treat was as a reward for drinking, came to like the drink more and more over the four weeks (as would be expected from the increased familiarity). However, children who were led to believe that the treat was a reward for drinking came to like it less and less. If drinking the beverage was seen as a means of 'earning' the treat it became less attractive rather than more attractive, even though drinking it was rewarded on each occasion. The same results were obtained if praise from an adult, rather than a tangible treat, was provided, or if the treat was made dependent on consuming a certain amount, rather than any, of the novel drink. Why should this be so? It seems that rewarding a child for something it was going to do anyway takes away or undercuts its 'natural' motivation. It is as though if you do it for no reward, as a free choice, you are more committed. Whatever the reason, these results imply that in the long term parents will produce the opposite effect to what they intend if they use rewards to encourage their children to eat up foods that they dislike.

The development of disgust

The growing child develops new capacities and abilities, and these affect its developing food preferences. The development of independent movement, of attachment to some adults and unease with others, of the capacity to communicate wishes to adults, and above all of language and of the intellect, all influence the development of food habits. Relatively primitive forms of learning such as 'mere exposure' operate from conception onwards, while more sophisticated forms of learning, such as social influence, can begin only once the child has developed a wide range of mental abilities. Learning to speak and think allows further development, for instance in the reasons given for rejecting foods; here there is a clear developmental sequence from the age of three years till adulthood.

Reasons for not eating

Very young children give only two explanations for not eating, distaste or danger: 'it's horrible' or 'it's poisonous'. Distaste is an immediate emotional response to the taste of the substance; the mirror image of liking, for example, sweet foods; it involves no thought or reflection and is evident from birth. Danger is a recognition that substances (such as poisonous mushrooms) may taste pleasant but have harmful consequences; it requires the capacity to imagine future events and see their connection with present actions. When very young children (of say, three years of age) reject substances (such as poisonous) because of danger, they also use distaste as a reason. They believe that all dangerous substances taste unpleasant.

Slightly older children can reject substances on grounds of danger alone. A further stage is rejection based purely on the idea of the substance, where the child explains its reaction as: 'It's just the idea of what it is.' Rejection just based on the idea occurs even though the substance in question (e.g. grass-hoppers) may be a potential foodstuff and is not seen as dangerous. This is close to what adults would call 'disgust'. In a study of American children and adults rejection based on disgust was never seen in three- or four-year-olds, but occurred in twenty-two per cent of seven-year-olds, seventy-eight per cent of ten-year-olds, and a hundred per cent of adults, particularly when referring to substances such as insects and dog faeces.

A reason that appears even later is rejection because of association, where just having been in contact with something that is 'taboo' renders any foodstuff unacceptable. Refusal of a glass of milk because the glass had previously contained a worm would be an example of this; most such examples involve the notion of 'contamination', which is relatively late to appear. It could not occur till imaginative capacities had developed strongly. A last reason for rejecting foods which emerges quite late applies to inappropriate combinations, such as ice cream and roast meat.

Hot dog with chocolate sauce is more acceptable than 'doggie-doo'

Thus some foods that are accepted quite happily by three- or four-year-olds will be rejected by older children or adults, and it is impossible for the young child to reject them for the same reason as the older one until he has developed sufficiently intellectually. One study which demonstrated this compared the acceptability of foods to children ranging in age from one and a half years to five years. Children were encouraged to eat samples of foods that would appear to adults to be disgusting or harmful, or to be combined in an unacceptable way. They were also offered non-foods (such as paper). Most children, whatever their age, ate 'unacceptable combinations' such as hot dog with chocolate sauce. The biggest difference in attitude was towards 'dangerous foods'. The children were offered what looked like washing-up liquid (but was in fact a harmless concoction); eighty per cent of the youngest children drank some, but only ten per cent of the oldest children did so. 'Disgusting foods' proved less acceptable with older children. A convincing cocoction of peanut butter with other edible substances was introduced as 'doggie doo' and eaten by fifty-five per cent of the youngest children and twelve per cent of the oldest. Non-foods such as paper or the green leaf of a plant proved acceptable to half of the children, regardless of their age. The youngest children were certainly omnivorous, but by the age of five years they had acquired the ability to reject food on the basis of danger or disgust. More subtle concepts, such as the idea of inappropriate combinations, take longer to develop.

Conclusion

From conception onwards we learn from our experiences to like some foods and to dislike others. The only instincts that we have are the ability to learn from our experiences and inborn preferences for sweet tastes as against others. Even these are strengthened or weakened by our experiences. Our earliest forms of learning are very crude ('mere exposure'), but as we develop into more social creatures we learn from other people, usually parents and other children. At first we learn what is food, and then we learn what not to eat. As our intellect and imagination develop we can learn in other ways. The preferences we acquire in childhood tend to be the strongest and to last through life, but learning does not stop once we become adults. In the next chapter we look at some of the ways in which we continue to learn.

4

Adults learn to eat

Adults continue to learn from their experiences with food all through their lives, usually without realising it. Many of the learning processes are subtle and beyond conscious awareness; some are dramatic and puzzling. Sometimes adults learn through the same processes as children (e.g. 'mere exposure'), but other processes are uniquely adult. The most important advances in our knowledge about human appetite show that it often runs counter to intuition and common sense. It is also clear that everyone cannot learn to like anything; there are limits to what we can learn.

What is safe to eat? The omnivore's problem

If you were designing omnivores like human beings how would you prevent them from poisoning themselves? Omnivores eat any kind of foodstuffs, animal or vegetable, but they are not born knowing which substances are nutritious and which are poisonous. It is not obvious which are which: if you saw a mushroom in the woods, could you tell whether it was poisonous, nutritious, or an hallucinogenic 'magic mushroom' that could send you on a 'trip'? Knowing what is what is no problem when you learn from other people and eat the same food again and again. Nevertheless omnivores do encounter new foods and need a way of avoiding being poisoned. Humans do die from mushroom poisoning. The problem becomes very clear when you travel to different countries with different plants and animals. Captain Cook's exploration of the Pacific faced him with a wide variety of new species. Even though he was able to learn from the inhabitants, in 1774 he nearly died after eating a particular kind of fish in New Caledonia. 'About three or four o'clock in the morning we were seized with an extraordinary weakness in all our limbs attended with a numbness or sensation like to that caused by exposing one's hands or feet to a fire after having been pinched much by frost. I had almost lost the sense of feeling nor could I distinguish between light and heavy bodies.' The fish that nearly killed him was a puffer fish, rather like the fugu fish so prized in Japan. Even taking the advice of local inhabitants did not protect him from being poisoned.

Food aversions

There are so many toxic plants and creatures that it would be impossible for omnivores to be born knowing which was which. Instead evolution has equipped us with the ability to learn to avoid foods that have made us sick in the past, which protects us from repeating the experience. Consider the following example. A colleague of the author used to eat doughnuts with his morning coffee most days. One day when coming down with flu he felt ill and was sick shortly after eating a doughnut. He then spent several days off work, ill in bed. Understanding that it was the flu rather than the doughnut that had made him sick he was surprised to find that the next time he went to eat a doughnut he felt sick and couldn't eat any at all. He had developed an aversion to the food, and this has lasted for five years to date. His is a fairly common experience, called food aversion learning, which about one person in three experiences at some time. This very primitive but highly effective form of learning does not depend on thought (in this instance it occurred despite it!) and betrays our omnivorous origins; it protects us from eating foods that may have made us sick.

Food aversions develop to foods that are eaten at roughly the same time as nausea is experienced, whatever the real cause of that nausea may be. Aversions are intense dislikes; they prevent us from eating the food, usually because we feel sick or unwell. They can develop in a wide range of circumstances when food is associated with nausea, whether this is caused by seasickness, illness or, indeed, something wrong with the food itself. This form of learning is of protective value to omnivores because many naturally occurring poisons cause nausea, and so 'once bitten, twice shy'. (Toxic substances in plants – 'secondary substances' – have evolved for the sole purpose of protecting the plant from being eaten by humans and other animals and represent attempts by the plant world to strike back and protect itself against the animal world.) Food aversions are of interest not only because they show a more primitive side of our nature, but also because they have important practical applications.

Taste aversions as a special form of conditioning

Taste aversion learning is a form of classical conditioning. Although many people use the term 'conditioning' in a wide sense to describe various forms of persuasion or ways in which people influence one another, it has a technical, very precise meaning. It describes a form of learning first studied in detail by Ivan Pavlov, a Russian physiologist working before the Russian revolution. In honour of him it is sometimes called 'Pavlovian conditioning'. This is a form of learning by association in which new associations are formed between stimuli (such as the taste of a food) and responses (such as nausea). The response becomes 'attached' to the stimulus. This occurs when the new stimulus is repeatedly presented at the same time as an event that produces the response; the new stimulus gradually acquires the capacity to produce the response itself. Conditioning can develop without any conscious awareness, and works particularly well when the responses to be conditioned are emotions.

As an example, two British psychologists showed that it was possible to condition the sexual responses of males to a stimulus that was entirely neutral for them – a picture of leather boots. Volunteers were shown a series of erotic slides which reliably produced sexual arousal. Interspersed with these were slides of boots; this new stimulus – the sight of boots – was associated with the response – sexual arousal – and gradually became able to produce this itself. After a number of pairings just viewing the slide of the boots produced a measurable increase in sexual arousal in the volunteers.

Once established, the new habit cannot be voluntarily overcome. An example is the conditioning of the 'let-down reflex' in lactating women. This can be conditioned to stimuli associated with babies so that, for example, hearing a baby cry in the street can trigger the reflex, so that milk sprays from the mother's nipples. A great deal of research into Pavlovian conditioning has established the circumstances in which it occurs most easily.

Taste aversion learning is a clear example of classical conditioning, but it is remarkable in several ways. Most forms of conditioning require many episodes of association for the habit to gradually build up, but taste aversions are fully developed after one episode. In most instances of conditioning timing is crucial; it is necessary for the response to be induced within seconds of the 'trigger' stimulus. In contrast taste aversions develop even if there is a gap of several hours between, say, eating and being sick. Taste aversion is an exceptional example of robust conditioning that develops easily, presumably because of its survival value. The only other example of conditioning in humans that does not fit the usual pattern is the acquisition of phobias (irrational fears) through the experience of fear or anxiety in a certain situation; the anxiety response becomes 'attached' to some aspect of the situation and occurs again whenever the person is faced with that aspect. Thus, for example, a diabetic was taken ill on a bus; he felt anxious and fearful lest he should fall into a diabetic coma; when he next went on a bus the feelings recurred. Like taste aversions, conditioned fears can be acquired in a robust manner.

The natural history of taste aversions

Taste aversions occur quite commonly in humans; surveys show that about thirty-eight per cent of both men and women have experienced them at some time and that most were acquired through the pairing of tasting the food and nausea. People are more likely to acquire aversions to foods that they are not very familiar with or which they dislike, and to strong tasting foods rather than weak tasting ones. Once acquired, aversions can persist for many years. Although they are usually very specific they can even spread to include other similar foods. A man who developed an aversion to curry gradually found that he could not eat any kind of spicy food at all. As time goes by some aversions gradually wither away and disappear, usually for no apparent reason.

Aversions tend to be directed more often towards protein foods (such as fish or meat), rather than carbohydrates (such as cakes or bread). Nearly a quarter of aversions are directed towards alcoholic drinks, which are often the cause of the aversion-producing nausea. Although aversions develop at any age they do seem to start most often in childhood, with the peak occurring between six and twelve years of age. As we saw in Chapter 2, aversions that occur during pregnancy usually develop during the first three months, when sickness is at its most frequent, encouraging the development of aversions through conditioning. That aversions develop particularly easily to protein foods rather than to others (e.g.

carbohydrates) is probably related to the fact that protein foods more often become toxic when they decay. It may be a greater advantage to be 'turned off' potentially harmful foods.

Food aversions may seem exotic, but they can have practical applications.

Eliminating the side effects of chemotherapy

Many powerful drugs used in the treatment of cancer produce nausea as a distressing side-effect. As a result many patients develop taste aversions to foods that they ate in the hours before receiving treatment. Sometimes these aversions produce lasting changes in food preferences so that patients become unable to eat or enjoy some of their usual foods. This, together with other appetite disturbances caused by the cancer, could lead to sufferers having an inadequate diet. Illness is not a time when changes in diet are easy to make. Research has established that conditioning, rather than any direct effects of the illness, is responsible for the development of aversions in these patients. Experiments have, for example, had patients taste a novel type of ice cream either shortly before receiving chemotherapy or on some other day. When their liking for the ice cream was measured again several days later, those who had received it before chemotherapy showed a much greater dislike for it; seventy-nine per cent of them developed an aversion to it, but virtually none of the others did. Eating it for the first time just before having chemo-therapy 'turned them off' it. Nausea can also be conditioned to other aspects of the treatment setting, such as the building in which it occurs. As a result the patient becomes ill just by going for treatment and can become much more distressed by these conditioned responses than by the immediate effects of the life-saving treatment. Knowing about the processes of conditioning allows us to understand how this can occur and helps us prevent or eliminate these conditioned responses.

One useful strategy was discovered as a by-product of the type of experiment above, in which cancer patients tasted a novel flavoured ice cream before receiving chemotherapy. Fewer patients who ate the unfamiliar food before receiving chemotherapy later developed aversions to their usual foods than did other patients who didn't eat it. This suggests that exposure to an unfamiliar food before drug treatment may have a protective effect – in isolating the nausea; further research is presently being carried out to see how valuable this might be. Once aversions have been developed they need to be de-conditioned. There is a whole field of endeavour, called behaviour therapy, which attempts to apply conditioning techniques therapeutically, and which has developed ways of unlearning acquired responses. This approach is now being applied to the problem of nausea being triggered by the treatment setting. One aim has been to help patients become deeply relaxed, both physically and mentally, before and during each chemotherapy session. They learn to relax by such means as hypnosis or muscle relaxation exercises and, once relaxed, use their capacity to generate pleasant visual images. They learn to focus their attention on these rather than on aspects of the treatment setting to which nausea has been conditioned. Learning to develop and use vivid relaxing imagery can help to unlearn the conditioned response. Relaxation training helps because deep relaxation prevents or dampens down the muscle activity in the stomach and throat that accompanies the development of nausea.

These fairly straightforward procedures have been found to eliminate or reduce nausea and untoward emotional reactions to the treatment, and even to reduce pulse rate and blood pressure during treatment. These treatments are still being developed and strengthened and approaches along these lines may well help to reduce nausea conditioned to foods and treatment settings.

Controlling coyotes

A second application of what we know about taste aversions has been to the problem of predation by coyotes. Coyotes are wolf-like creatures who inhabit North America and attack and eat sheep. Traditionally farmers have tried to control coyote populations by hunting them, or poisoning them, but these measures have had very limited effects. The problem is that once one set of predators has been killed others can move in from a neighbouring area. Sometimes hunting can even have a beneficial effect on the coyote population, killing off weak or unwell individuals so that only the strongest are left to breed. It seemed logical to help free-living coyotes acquire taste aversions to sheep so that they would stop eating sheep and instead feed on other creatures such as rodents. This was first tried with captive coyotes and the results were encouraging. Coyotes were fed with the corpses of either lambs or rabbits which had been adulterated with lithium chloride, a salt-like substance that causes sickness. After eating the doctored meat on just two or three occasions the captive coyotes developed clear aversions towards it; they avoided eating the flesh of the species they had been presented with, but ate the flesh of other animals avidly. The aversion affected not only their actual feeding habits, but also other habits, such as attacking the animal. Those fed on adulterated lamb did not attack lambs when given the opportunity, and those fed adulterated rabbit did not attack rabbits. A similar effect was reported for captive wolves fed upon a package of sheep flesh adulterated with lithium chloride. When tested in a pen with an adult sheep the wolves charged it but did not pursue their attack further; as time went by the sheep made more threatening movements and appeared to dominate the wolves.

Once the approach was found to work in controlled surroundings with captive creatures, the next stage was to apply it in a real-life setting on a ranch where coyotes regularly took sheep. The first study of this kind was carried out in 1975 on a 3,000 acre sheep ranch in the State of Washington in the USA; the carcasses of sheep that had died from natural causes were injected with lithium chloride solution so that coyotes feeding on them would become ill and thus develop an aversion to sheep. Once the adulterated corpses were spread around the ranch the numbers of sheep lost to the predators dropped by a third. After that first successful experiment the technique was adopted in nearly a dozen projects in the USA and Canada. The results varied considerably. In one very large scale study in Saskatchewan in Canada the taste aversion procedure was applied to forty-six herds over three years. The numbers of sheep lost were dramatically reduced. In ten herds where precise estimates could be made, the cost of sheep lost dropped from $53,500 a year before the project to $6,800 a year during it. Yet, because of the difficulties in evaluating the effects on predation, experts still disagree about the technique, and a fierce controversy about it continues.

Stopping eating and drinking

A third practical application of taste aversions to real-life problems is in the control of appetites in the treatment of obesity and alcoholism. The possibility of harnessing this naturally occurring phenomenon for beneficial ends is obvious. If aversions spontaneously develop in many people towards alcohol then why not aid alcoholics to stop drinking by helping them develop aversions to their favourite drinks? If slimmers find it hard to stop themselves eating particular foods then why not help them develop aversions to them? This has been the rationale for the development of aversion therapy techniques for these problems, in which the patient tastes the substance and then experiences nausea. The means of inducing nausea have been various but have included injections of nausea-producing drugs, hypnosis, inhaling cigarette smoke (by non-smokers), and imagining unpleasant scenes. An example of the latter, for someone who wants to be 'turned off' chocolate bars, is the following:

> Imagine the following scene as clearly and vividly as possible, as if you were actually there, trying to feel the feelings as well as 'seeing' what happens to yourself. Picture yourself walking along the road, and going into a shop to buy some chocolate. As you start to unwrap the bar and smell the aroma of the chocolate you

get a very queasy feeling deep in your stomach. You begin feeling weak and ill, as though you want to be sick. You start to put a bit of the chocolate into your mouth and feel the sick feeling rising up into your throat and mouth. As you start to chew the chocolate you feel terrible, and begin to vomit. Your clothes are covered in the stuff and you feel so embarrassed as people look at you retching in the street. You feel so horrible and sick, and the disgusting liquid reeks of the smell of chocolate.

Do such charming techniques produce aversions? And do they help in controlling the appetite? There is evidence that these techniques can produce lasting aversions to particular foods and drinks, aversions strong enough to reverse the body's 'giveaway' reactions to being presented with preferred substances, such as increased salivation and heart rate and dilation of the pupil. It is interesting that we can form aversions to food we like as well as to unfamiliar or disliked foods. Unfortunately these changes of preference are not usually sufficient to implement a complete change of behaviour. The reason for this is that the aversions are very specific. If the dieter is 'turned off' one problem food there are many more attractive foods to provide temptation; if the problem drinker no longer finds whisky attractive, there are many other forms in which alcohol can be consumed. And, just as the nauseated responses of the cancer patient can be deconditioned, so determined drinkers can drink themselves 'through' the nausea and thus help to decondition themselves. Aversive techniques have been found to have no real value in helping to produce weight loss, and little value in the treatment of alcohol abuse.

Positive conditioning

Can conditioning work in the opposite direction? If eating foods is paired with pleasant or beneficial experiences, do the foods become more attractive? If the ability to form taste aversions easily has the biological value of protecting us from consuming poisons, then do we have the reverse ability to guide us towards nutritious foods?

Experiments with rats have shown that this can occur in some ways. Foods associated with recovery from illness are preferred, while those associated with illness are rejected. In one experiment rats received a daily injection of a nausea-inducing drug for several weeks. On each of these 'illness' days they drank a flavoured liquid just before having the injection; during the next few weeks while recovering from this illness they drank a different flavoured liquid each day. Half of the rats drank grape juice on 'illness' days and then milk on 'recovery' days; the other half drank milk and then grape juice. The results show that, as would be expected, the flavour associated with illness (whichever it is) is rejected, even during recovery. The flavour associated with recovery becomes progressively more preferred, showing a positive conditioning effect.

Most demonstrations of positive conditioning in rats use recovery from illness or recovery from vitamin deficiency as the positive event. Thus foods to which thiamine has been added come to be preferred after thiamine-deficient rats have fed on them, and the preferences continue even after the deficiency is cleared up and the thiamine is withdrawn. It is not that the rats 'know' in advance that these foods are good for them; rather they learn to like them as a result of their experiences with them. It is the same as coming to prefer the medicine that is associated with recovery.

Does positive conditioning occur in humans? The case of the 'salt boy' (see Chapter 2) who needed to consume foods rich in sodium because of an inborn medical disorder, showed that he was capable of learning from his experience that salty foods, and especially pure salt, were beneficial to him, and thus he came to prefer them. However, because he was always in need of sodium until his premature death we do not know whether the very strong preference for salty foods would have persisted once that need had been satisfied. In the case of the child in Clara Davis's 'self-service diet' who ate cod-liver oil while ill with rickets, the boy stopped taking the 'medicine' once the rickets had healed, thus failing to show a 'medicine effect' – a continued liking for medicine as demonstrated by the rats.

Is there a real 'medicine effect' with humans? Do the tastes of medicines that cause reductions in nausea or some other gastrointestinal distress become more liked after successful treatment? Attempts to answer this question have failed to find any evidence that this does happen. Positive conditioning seems to be a much weaker phenomenon than aversive conditioning, possibly because it is easier to specify foods that should not be eaten than ones that should. Extreme circumstances are probably necessary to develop marked and lasting preferences.

It would be interesting to have examined the long-term preferences of the Portuguese sailors suffering from scurvy, who in 1499 landed on a Caribbean island and were cured of the disease after eating the limes they found growing there. They called the island Curaçao, which is Portuguese for 'cure', in recognition of this event. In a parallel with the study of rats that were fed one food while ill and another during recovery, we might predict that these sailors should subsequently have liked limes and disliked their shipboard diet. It is also possible to see an 'illness effect' in the aftermath of famines when foods on which people just survived are rejected. After the Great Famine in Ireland in the 1840s berries and other vegetation were derided as 'famine food'; it is likely that this was in part due to aversive conditioning.

Both aversive conditioning and positive conditioning are relatively crude ways of learning about food. However they point towards what has been one of the biggest breakthroughs in our understanding of our appetite – the notion that we learn about foods from the consequences of eating them.

Learning from the consequences of eating

Aversion learning and positive conditioning are crude ways

for our bodies to learn from our experiences with food because they are relatively rare events and, especially in the case of taste aversions, absolute in their effects, stopping all consumption of the food. The body's needs are actually more subtle and variable, and such crude 'blocks' can only make sense as 'emergency' responses when life is in danger. We control our day-to-day intake of food making more sophisticated use of the same information employed in taste aversion conditioning – relating foods to the consequences we experience from eating them. It is as though we learn from each experience of consuming foods and expect the same response the next time we eat them, and this controls what we eat and how much we eat of which food. This is not a conscious process; we are only consciously aware of a few of our mental processes and, in fact, wouldn't be able to cope if we had to concentrate on all our actions. Walking along a busy street while carrying on a conversation with two other people just wouldn't be possible if we had to concentrate our conscious minds on all our actions, the brain would just be overloaded. Carrying out intelligent actions, modifying behaviour in the light of events, does not necessarily require conscious thought, and this is certainly true in the case of controlling food intake.

This process works like the Pavlovian conditioning that we have already considered, although in a continuous and un-dramatic way. So important is conditioning thought to be by one of the world's leading experts on human eating patterns, David Booth of Birmingham University, that he summed up the issue in the title of an article: 'Satiety and appetite are conditioned reactions'.

What controls satiety?

What does satiety actually mean? Consider the problem of controlling the size of a meal of a particular food. How do we know when to stop eating, when our energy need from that meal is satisfied? Satiety cannot develop as the result of digestion because this process takes too long – it would only work if we ate large meals very slowly for several hours. Nor can satiety develop on the basis of recognising what food is being eaten after the first mouthful. If this occurred then it would develop even if nothing more were then eaten, so that insufficient energy would be ingested.

Instead, Booth suggested that satiety is a conditioned response, arising out of our previous experiences with that food. The consequences of previous experiences include the analysis of the food as a result of digestion, including knowledge of its energy content. We 'anticipate' (although not in a conscious sense) that future encounters with the same food will have similar consequences; this accounts for the control of energy intake (and thus meal size) through the development of satiety.

In one study of this phenomenon, subjects were provided with a free lunch of soup and sandwiches for eight days; each day they drank a fixed amount of soup and then ate as many small sandwich bits as they wished. There were two flavours of low-calorie soup and to one of these was added some soluble starch, which produces satiety after an hour (i.e. after the end of the meal). The 'normal' soup contained twenty-five calories, while the other contained 210 calories. The subjects didn't know about the energy values of the soups, but had them on alternate days. If Booth is right then they should have recognised unconsciously that one flavour meant that the soup was high in energy. The result should have been a gradual reduction in the size of the sandwich meal eaten after that flavour soup, in order to keep a standard energy intake. There should also have been a gradual increase in the size of the sandwich meal taken after the low-energy flavour. This is in fact what happened. The subjects' brains began to anticipate the calorie content of the meal and produced satiety at the appropriate time, even though there was no conscious awareness of this.

Usually previous experiences with a food form a valid basis for anticipating the consequences of future experiences; they become invalid when faced with a food which appears and

74

tastes identical to the known food, but is in fact very different in its chemical composition.

Developments in food technology have produced, for example, low-calorie soups and drinks that cannot be distinguished by the untrained tongue from high-calorie counterparts. Substituting one of these for the high-calorie version would be expected to produce the same degree of satiety on the first occasion it was consumed; however, in the light of this, satiety would gradually develop more and more slowly on subsequent meals of this substance as the implications of each learning experience gradually modified anticipations and the control of future meals. Thus our appetite for a meal depends on our past experiences with similar meals, and satiety at a particular meal depends not on what is in this meal, but on what was in similar meals we ate in the past. It has been shown that even the appetites of three-year-old children work on this principle.

Davis's account of children's reactions to her 'self-service' regime suggests that they can learn from their experiences with food as soon as they are weaned. The fact that the children regularly took salt in order to obtain needed sodium, even though it seemed distasteful to them, suggests this. Perhaps the most revealing observation made by Davis was in her account of the infants' reactions to foods during the first few days of the study. She described how the children sampled each food at first and then gradually developed clear preferences. 'Their choices were apparently wholly random; they tried not only foods but chewed hopefully the clean spoon, dishes, the edge of the tray, or a piece of paper on it. Their faces showed expressions of surprise, followed by pleasure, indifference or dislike. Within the first few days they began to reach eagerly for some foods and to neglect others, so that definite tastes grew under our eyes.' The children learned from their experiences with the range of natural foods presented to them, presumably guided by the processes of post-ingestional conditioning that have been described.

Learning by conditioning is a very powerful way of learning

from our experiences with food and it explains how satiety is recognised.

Can we learn to like anything?

The reader's attention has been drawn to the similarities between learning a first language and learning the food rules of a culture. Almost any new-born child could be brought up to speak any language, or to accept the food of any culture. The 'almost' is there because there are some genetically determined characteristics that limit what can be learned. A simple example comes from our perception of taste. There is a chemical substance called phenylthiocarbamide (PTC), which some people can taste as bitter and others cannot taste at all; whether or not a person can taste PTC is determined by the presence or absence of a particular gene. If someone cannot detect this taste then he cannot learn to either like it or dislike it, and so from conception onwards his potential ability to acquire taste preferences is limited. Interestingly enough, there does seem to be some biological value in tasting PTC in some settings. PTC is very closely related to bitter tasting green vegetables such as spinach, and such vegetables have an anti-thyroid effect in people predisposed to goitre. Thus in areas of the world where iodine is scarce and people are vulnerable to goitre, for example the Andes, avoiding such bitter tasting vegetables is an advantage. In those circumstances being able to taste PTC can help protect people against thyroid disorders, and this is why PTC-tasters are more common in such areas.

Lactose intolerance

Adults who are able to enjoy drinking milk are unusual in global terms. They include North Europeans, American whites and African races such as the nomadic Fulani of West Africa and the Tussi of Uganda, who traditionally herd cows and goats. Amongst most of the world's population, as with most other mammals, milk is a food for the new-born. Adults develop lactose intolerance, the inability to digest lactose, which is one of the main constituents of milk, along with fats and proteins. Lactose is a sugar that is produced only by lactating (breastfeeding) mammals. It can be digested only by the action of lactase, an enzyme that converts lactose into two other sugars, glucose and galactose, which the body uses for fuel. Lactase is normally found in the small intestine of infant mammals, at a time when consumption of maternal milk is highest. It starts being produced during the later stages of pregnancy and tends to decline (in most species of mammals) after weaning. Amongst humans this is true of the Chinese, Arabs, Eskimos, Africans, Japanese, South American Indians, American blacks, Indians, Pakistanis, and Bangladeshis. When they consume milk (or unfermented milk products) they suffer a range of symptoms including a bloated feeling, stomach cramps, flatulence and diarrhoea; on occasions feeding lactose-intolerant children on milk has been found to cause malnutrition and even death. Lactose intolerance is transmitted genetically so that, from conception onwards, individuals with this characteristic have only a limited capacity to learn to like milk and milk products. In this and other ways new-born children do not have the ability to learn to like absolutely any food. The new-born infant is not an empty page, ready to be written on by experience; its genetic inheritance and prenatal experience have already marked it, in some cases indelibly.

Do our genes tell us what we like?

Apart from specific limitations such as lactose intolerance how far does our genetic inheritance influence our food preferences? There is evidence that intelligence and aspects of personality, such as emotionality, are influenced in this way; are our food likes and dislikes? Attempts have been made to answer this question by looking at twins. There are two kinds of twins – identical (monozygotic), who share the same genetic make-up, and fraternal (dizygotic), who are no more alike genetically than any pair of brothers or sisters. Identical twins often look identical; they develop from the same fertilised egg and are thus genetically identical, and of the same sex. Fraternal twins develop from two fertilised eggs at the same time and are therefore only as alike as two brothers or sisters born at different times; they can be of the same or different sexes. Some researchers have studied identical twins who were separated shortly after birth and then brought up without contact with one another. It was assumed that similarities between them would result from their identical genetic inheritance, while differences would be the result of their experiences in life. The similarities between reunited twins are often uncanny. In the book *Twins*, Peter Watson described a pair of male twins who had been separated soon after birth. When they were reunited as adults they found that they had the following in common:

  among other things they both
  – had married a woman named Linda, divorced her, and then married a woman called Betty
  – named their first son James Alan
  – had a dog called Tig
  – had worked part-time as a deputy sheriff, and in McDonalds
  – spent a holiday on the same short beach in Florida
  – liked stock-car racing
  – suffered from piles and tension headaches
  – bit their fingernails
  – preferred the same brand of beer.

Dramatic though these sets of coincidences are, how important or surprising are they? And how similar might the twins' food preferences be? What is important is to establish how likely it would be for two unrelated strangers of the same social backgrounds as the two twins to have the same food preferences. For example it would not be astonishing if two British twins chose the following meal for dinner from a menu in a restaurant: starter – prawn cocktail; main dish – steak and chips; sweet – black forest gâteau. It would not be surprising because this is the single most frequently ordered selection of dishes in Britain. (Thirty years ago the first course would have been tomato soup and the sweet apple pie and ice cream.) One or two coincidences are likely; it is the multiplication of coincidences that raises the possibility of genetic influence. The studies of twins separated at birth have not as yet established the degree of similarity in their food preferences, but do not tend to indicate that they are very closely matched. An alternative method of studying twins is to look at the food and taste preferences of identical twins and same-sex fraternal twins brought up together. The stronger the influence of genetics, the more likely it is that identical twins should resemble each other more closely than fraternal twins. If genetics had no influence at all then both sets of twins should show the same degree of similarity. The results of such studies fail to find any clear genetically determined preferences for particular tastes, or foods. The foods we enjoy are not determined by our genes, but by learning from our experiences.

Conclusion

Our tastes and preferences are limited by inborn characteristics but are not determined by them. They are affected by our experiences with taste and food from conception onwards, the most important processes being subtle conditioning. The most important inborn characteristic is the ability to learn from experience.

5

Mind over mouth

Why don't we eat what we need?

The nutritional wisdom that we use in childhood becomes less and less influential as we grow older. Why? More and more other influences come to bear on us and to override our biological wisdom. These include our thoughts and beliefs, our conscious attempts to control our food intake, and the nature of the food available. Each of these can distort and disturb our appetite in different ways so as to prevent it from operating 'naturally'.

Beliefs about food

Our beliefs about foods affect which ones we will eat and the amount we will consume. Many vegetarians don't eat meat because they believe that it is wrong (even though they might enjoy doing it); anti-racists don't eat South African oranges even though they might enjoy their taste, and couldn't distinguish them from other oranges. Today in Western countries more and more people eat foods like yoghurt and muesli because they believe that they will bring health. In

81

different cultures people learn to believe that health depends on a balanced diet, although the nature of that balance varies considerably. In China it is seen as a balance between 'hot' foods (yang) and 'cold' foods (yin) where 'hot' and 'cold' have little to do with temperature. Yang foods include stronger tasting, oily, richer, and spicy foods, fatty meat and peanuts, as well as alcoholic drinks. Yin foods are blander, lower in calories, and include fleshy vegetables, watercress and herbs, beans *and* crabs. Rice is a balanced food. The way food is cooked or prepared makes it 'hotter' or 'colder'; the following methods are in increasing order of 'hotness' – infusing in cold water, boiling, stir-frying, roasting, baking and deep-frying. The ideal balance point is different for men and women; men should be slightly to the 'hot' side of balance, whilst women should be slightly to the 'cool' side. Other cultures hold other sets of beliefs about which combinations of foods are desirable; the important fact is that beliefs influence the choice of foods.

Aphrodisiacs

No food acts directly on the brain to increase sexual desire, but almost every culture has believed that there are foods which are aphrodisiacs. The nature of aphrodisiacs varies from culture to culture, and from age to age. Men in twelfth century India ate the testicles of goats boiled in milk and sugar, because they believed that this would increase their potency. In Chaucer's *Canterbury Tales* sparrows' eggs and cooked sparrows were alleged to have aphrodisiac properties. In Elizabethan England foods that were believed to act in this way included prunes, which were served up in brothels, and the two exciting foods recently introduced from the New World – tomatoes (known as 'love apples' and whose un-usually vivid redness was associated with passion) and potatoes (which is why Shakespeare made Falstaff exclaim: 'Let the sky rain potatoes!' in *The Merry Wives of Windsor*). Napoleon's Josephine revived interest in the sweet potato, served sliced and sugared, and encouraged belief in its aphrodisiac qualities. Even today rhinos are slaughtered in Africa because men in some Far Eastern countries believe that rhino horn will restore their virility.

Many supposed aphrodisiacs are either novel, or resemble the sexual organs in some way (e.g. horns, antlers) or produce some form of stimulation or irritation (e.g. Spanish fly – a Mediterranean beetle, which is taken dried and crushed). An interesting range of supposed aphrodisiacs from the past (e.g. those mentioned in the *Kama Sutra*) include highly nutritious, energy-rich ingredients such as honey, eggs and milk. This would give an energy boost to malnourished people and a by-product of this might be to enhance sexual appetite.

On a more mundane level the role of thoughts and beliefs has been demonstrated in the laboratory. In a study carried out in Germany volunteers consumed a tablet and shortly afterwards ate lunch. Half of the tablets given out were vitamin pills, and half were a type of appetite suppressant (fenfluramine); half of the subjects who were given each type of tablet were told that it was an appetite suppressant (whether it was or not) and half were told that it was a vitamin tablet. The amount of food eaten at lunch was affected by what people believed their tablet to have contained, rather than what it actually did contain. Those who believed that they had taken an appetite suppressant consumed thirty per cent less than those who believed that they had consumed a vitamin tablet. What you believe can override what your body tells you.

Restraint

This is even more true if you are trying to control what you eat in order to lose weight. Exercising conscious control in this way can disrupt and distort the 'natural' control of appetite, and the more concerned you are about it, the greater the effect. Before we go any further look at the questionnaire below, and if you like, work out your score. You will then be able to see where you fit in in the section that follows.

Table 3   Restrained Eating Questionnaire

1   How often are you dieting?
    (a) never (b) rarely (c) sometimes (d) often (e) always
2   What is the maximum amount of weight (in pounds) that you
    have ever lost within one month?
    (a) 0–4 (b) 5–9 (c) 10–14 (d) 15–19 (e) 20+
3   What is your maximum weight gain (in pounds) within a week?
    (a) 0–1 (b) 1+–2 (c) 2+–3 (d) 3+–5(e) 5+
4   In a typical week, how much does your weight fluctuate (in
    pounds)?
    (a) 0–1 (b) 1+–2 (c) 2+–3 (d) 3+–5 (e) 5+
5   Would a weight fluctuation of 5 lbs affect the way you live your
    life?
    (a) not at all (b) slightly (c) moderately (d) very much
6   Do you eat sensibly in front of others and splurge alone?
    (a) never (b) rarely (c) often (d) always
7   Do you give too much time and thought to food?
    (a) never (b) rarely (c) often (d) always
8   Do you have feelings of guilt after overeating?
    (a) never (b) rarely (c) often (d) always
9   How conscious are you of what you are eating?
    (a) not at all (b) slightly (c) moderately (d) extremely
10 How many pounds over your desired weight were you at your
    maximum weight?
    (a) 0–1 (b) 1–5 (c) 6–10 (d) 11–20 (e) 21+

See p. 199 to work out your score.

This questionnaire gives you a score on the 'eating restraint scale', and is a measure of your conscious concern to control food intake, and thus bodyweight; it was produced in 1975 by two Canadian psychologists, Peter Herman and Janet Polivy. It has been used in many studies because the scores people get on it reveal something very important about them and allow psychologists to predict their eating habits. Those with high restraint scores behave very differently from those with low scores. The study of dietary restraint has also led to major insights into disorders such as bulimia nervosa and anorexia nervosa.

If your score is less than 11 you are an unrestrained eater; if it is greater than 19 you are a highly restrained eater; if it lies between 13 and 19 you are a moderately restrained eater. (Note that this is a fairly crude categorisation; a more sophisticated result is obtained from longer versions of the questionnaire.) Your score is a fairly good predictor of how you would behave under certain circumstances.

Imagine that you are taking part in the following experiment, having volunteered to be a subject for a 'study about taste'. You are given a flavoured milky drink to consume and afterwards fill in a questionnaire about how sweet, creamy, fruity etc. it tasted. Then you are shown into another room where there are three large dishes piled full of small sandwiches, a different flavour on each dish. You are told that you will be left alone for thirty minutes while you eat as many as you want and fill in further questionnaires about the taste of each type. How much difference would it make to what you do (i.e. how many sandwiches you eat) if you had been led to believe that the milky drink had been either (a) a calorie-rich milk shake, to which cream had been added, or (b) a virtually calorie-free drink for slimmers?

If you were an unrestrained eater it would make no difference at all, but if you were a highly restrained eater it would make a great deal of difference. You would in fact be very likely to eat much more if you believed that the drink was high in calories than if you believed it was a low-calorie drink (and more than the unrestrained eaters!). As you have probably guessed, this pattern would be revealed whether or not there was any difference between the drinks; this is a psychological effect, not a physiological effect. It is the opposite of energy regulation (where consuming high-calorie drinks would be expected to lead to compensation, in the form of smaller sandwich meals) and so it has been called counter-regulation. It is as if the restrained eater (who is very conscious of energy intake) says to himself something like: 'Now I've eaten that, I've taken so much energy in, and gone so far over my diet, that it doesn't matter how much more I eat.' Having 'gone too far' dissipates or dissolves the self-control that the restrained eater normally shows.

Provoking binges in the laboratory

Similar sorts of experiments have been carried out where the first part of the experiment is changed. Instead of affecting subjects' beliefs about the calorie value of the drink the experimenters manipulated the subject's mood (by causing some subjects to feel mildly depressed). In another some subjects were given alcohol whilst others drank a placebo. In each case the manipulation affected the amount of food restrained eaters ate but had no effect on that eaten by unrestrained eaters. Restrained eaters ate more after consuming alcohol or when they felt depressed. Each of these three types of procedures produced counterregulation, 'releasing' eating that is normally inhibited and restrained. Research has shown that other disinhibitors include eating a meal with companions who eat large amounts of food, and knowing that you will be eating a high-calorie meal in the near future.

Binges in real life

What has all this got to do with real life outside the laboratory? A great deal. There are very close similarities between counterregulation (in normal people in the laboratory) and the binge eating that is a feature of such disorders as bulimia nervosa and anorexia nervosa. Binge eating tends to be more rapid and to involve much more food, but occurs particularly often when the sufferer has either eaten more than she (and it normally is a she) had allowed herself, or has consumed alcohol, or is in a negative mood state, or all three of these. Such sufferers tend to score near the maximum on the restrained eating questionnaire. As we shall see in Chapter 10, our understanding of counterregulation enables us to understand, treat (and possibly prevent) these serious disorders. Further, as we shall see in Chapter 9, studies of relapse in obese people who have successfully lost weight find that the relapse tends to occur most often in the following two situations (in order of importance): negative mood states when alone, and happy social situations. If we view ex-obese persons as restrained eaters then it is not surprising that this should be so, and implies that certain treatment approaches ('relapse prevention training') would be helpful in preparing them to prevent relapse. These are examples of the practical applications of our notion of 'restrained eating'. But what is perhaps most important is the clear way in which conscious attempts to control food intake can override, distort, and pervert our natural controls. 'Counterregulation' shows why we don't eat what we need.

Eyes and nose over stomach; what we see is what we want

Just imagine yourself in the following setting and consider how you would react. You are a space traveller on a journey to one of the furthest planets, which is going to take several months to complete. You live in a fairly large metallic-looking compartment rather like a cockpit. Because of the low-gravity environment your food for the journey has to come from a food dispenser; you press buttons to indicate your choice of food and then place your mouth over a nozzle. When you press a button a mouthful of the foodstuff is ejected into your mouth. The food is delicious but you cannot see it or smell it, but only taste it. When you are ready for your next mouthful you press the button again and a further bite-size portion enters your mouth. How would you feel about this method of eating? Would you look forward to mealtimes? How often would you eat, compared to now? Would you lose weight or gain weight during the journey?

Hunger comes from outside

Most people who imagine themselves in this situation feel that much of the pleasure of eating would be gone, that they would eat less often, get less pleasure from eating, and lose weight.

This is because 'space feeding' eliminates all sensations except the flavour of the food, so that it becomes more and more like refuelling, and many reminders of food are entirely absent. The example illustrates the fact that for most people the major influence on appetite and eating is not inside us but outside us. The sight and smell of food stimulate appetite far more than 'internal' feelings of hunger etc. It's a common experience to go to the fridge for something specific like milk and to see plates of such foods as cream cake or cheese and only then to start to feel peckish. Contact with such sensory reminders of foods stimulates appetite in such a way as to swamp and override the 'natural controls' of regulation that we have discussed. Sensory stimulation can achieve its effects without our being aware of it, and some people are particularly vulnerable to this.

Turned on by food

Whether or not you'll eat, how much you'll eat, and even the style in which you'll eat are strongly controlled by the setting in which you eat. For most people even imagining eating a favourite food can produce physical reactions that usually occur when you eat. These reactions include obvious things such as salivation, but also more subtle signs such as an increase in the size of the pupils and invisible changes such as the release of insulin into the bloodstream. We vary in how much our bodies are 'turned on' by contact with food, and some people are extremely susceptible to this influence. Experiments have shown that just smelling a steak cooking can produce dramatic reactions in some people, which prepare the body to eat, and make them physically as well as psychologically hungry. It had been suggested by a leading American psychologist, Stanley Schachter, that obese people were more turned on by food than non-obese people, but this has been found not to be the case. However, there are many obese persons who are affected particularly strongly in this way, and it is only feasible for them to diet successfully if they arrange their lives in such a way as to minimise contact with food stimuli. As we shall see in Chapter 9, some treatment programmes teach them to make very detailed changes in their way of life so as to reduce temptation – including taking the lightbulb out of the fridge, storing food in opaque containers, etc. Paradoxically, people who are most easily turned on by food can last longer without feeling hungry when there are no food stimuli around, as in the spaceship situation just described. Another situation where this is shown is in religious fasts (such as Yom Kippur) where no food is present. People whose appetite is triggered the most strongly by external factors can fast with less hunger than others. In the spaceship they would lose weight.

Most people's food choices are strongly influenced by the strength of food stimuli. The sight of food is important. Studies in self-service cafeterias have found that putting foods under a very bright display lamp doubles the probability that they will be selected and that merely closing the transparent sliding lid of a deep freeze halves the amount of ice cream chosen.

Smell is a very influential form of contact with food, as important as taste. In one study people tried to identify small portions of food placed directly on their tongues. Half of the time they could smell normally, but half of the time they could smell only purified air, which was being pumped through their nostrils. When smelling normally the subjects could correctly identify sixty per cent of the foods; when they were prevented from smelling the food on their tongues they could identify only ten per cent. Coffee was correctly identified by ninety-five per cent of persons when smelling normally, but by none when smell was removed. Smell contributes to overall flavour, and is more important the more delicate the taste of the food. For reasons that are not understood, right-handed people have a more sensitive sense of smell in their right nostril, and left-handed people have a more sensitive left nostril. The absence of a sense of smell (anosmia) is much more common than most people think. Wordsworth was anosmic – and this is reflected in his poetry by the absence of imagery based on smell.

The sense of taste is powerful, but does not work at a distance, as smell and sight do, and is less sensitive than smell. Humans have some 9,000 tastebuds, as compared with the twenty-four of the chicken, 350 of the parrot, 17,000 of the rabbit, and 25,000 of the catfish. Tastebuds register the distinct tastes of sweet, sour, bitter and salty, but can be fooled by naturally occurring substances. 'Miracle fruit', for example, is a West African plant with red berries the size of olives; eating the berries distorts taste so that sour things taste sweet. Lemons taste like oranges and grapefruit taste sweet. Taste preferences change with experience, so that if people take in extra salt each day they come to like it more (but only if they taste it – swallowing tasteless salt capsules has no effect). Sweet preferences decline naturally between the early teenage years and young adulthood.

The senses of smell and taste appear to be more closely linked to emotions than are the other senses, and can summon up associated memories more completely and vividly – the classic example being in Proust's *Swann's Way*, where the taste of a cake dunked in tea brought alive vivid memories of childhood. The sight of the cake had no effect – only the combination of its taste with that of tea: 'When from a long-distant past nothing subsists, after the people are dead, after the things are broken and scattered, taste and smell alone, more fragile but more enduring, more unsubstantial, more persistent, more faithful, remain poised a long time, like souls, remembering, waiting, hoping, amid the ruins of all the rest; and bear unflinchingly . . . the vast structure of recollection.'

Variety is the spice of food

One factor that has particularly potent effects on appetite (even without our conscious awareness) is the variety of foods available; other things being equal, the greater the variety, the more food is eaten. Food variety influences many species, and can overcome the energy regulation of the rat. In Chapter 2 the rat was described as being much better than humans at adjusting the quantity of food eaten according to its energy content; it balances its energy needs and energy intake and so maintains a fairly constant weight. The one situation in which that balancing ability can be swamped is when it is presented with a wide variety of tasty foodstuffs. Rats fed on pellets of chow maintain a constant energy intake and weight; rats fed with chocolate bars, biscuits, cheese crackers, potato crisps, and chow increase their energy intake and double their weight.

Humans behave very similarly. Barbara Rolls carried out experiments with different kinds of food at Oxford University and found variety to have a strong effect. People eating sandwiches for lunch eat thirty per cent more if they choose from a selection of four different flavours than if there is just one flavour available. There is a similar increase in the quantity eaten if there are more flavours of yoghurt offered, or even different shapes of pasta (bow-ties, hoops and spaghetti as compared to any one of these). In one study twice as much ice cream was eaten if three flavours were available than if there was only one. In none of these studies did people who took part become aware of what was happening. The 'variety effect' is caused by the brain in an unconscious way, and is observed in other species. Something so fundamental and so widespread must have some evolutionary advantage, probably that if creatures do eat a wide range of foods they have a better chance of receiving adequate nutrients. The tendency has evolved because, over hundreds of generations, better-fed creatures are more likely to breed and pass on their genes to the next generation. However, this evolutionary change took place in one environment and may not have the same advantage in radically different circumstances, such as Western society today where there is such a profusion of processed foods.

Satiety is specific

How does the variety effect operate? The opposite of variety is monotony, and a monotonous diet soon becomes less interesting and therefore less appetising. After you have eaten one type of food (e.g. sausages), it becomes less appetising but other foods (e.g. bacon) remain just as appetising as they were before. Satiety is not a general state that cuts off the desire for all foods equally, even though the expression 'I'm full' implies that the stomach, like a bag, has been filled. Satiety is specific to particular foods. Therefore in a meal of sausages and bacon, if I eat sausages and no longer find them appetising, the bacon is still as appetising as if I hadn't eaten the sausages. And in a meal of sausage, bacon, and scrambled egg, if I eat sausage and then bacon and therefore find both of these less appealing, the scrambled egg still remains attractive. This is how variety works, by overcoming the satiety that develops to particular foods (called 'specific satiety'). The more dissimilar the foods, the greater the effect of variety of food intake. It is surprising that a variety effect can be triggered by foods that differ only in their shape (the pasta example above). Specific satiety can even develop on the basis of just the colour of small coloured chocolate sweets ('Smarties'); if red ones are eaten, they become less appetising, but ones of other colours (e.g. yellow, green) remain just as appealing – despite the fact that all of them taste identical! Variety is the spice of food!

Some people are more strongly affected by variety than others. Extroverted people enjoy experiencing a wide variety of sensations in all areas of life. This appears to be linked with the level of activity in part of the brain; it is highest in very introverted, reserved and solitary people and lowest in very extroverted, sociable and impulsive people. Humans have a need for a moderate level of this brain activity; marked extroverts have a need to increase theirs and marked introverts have a need to decrease theirs. It is important to distinguish between brain activity (which we have been discussing) and physical activity. Someone, such as an introvert, can have a high level of brain activity but be a quiet, sober, person. One way of increasing brain activity is to seek out stimulation in various forms; going on frightening rides at a funfair is one way of increasing stimulation and boosting brain activity level. Extroverts tend to be 'hungry' for stimulation, and therefore seek sensations. One area of sensation-seeking is in taste and other aspects of food. Several studies in America have found that people with a high need for sensation are more likely than others to eat more spicy foods, shellfish, foreign foods (e.g. Middle Eastern, Greek or Japanese) and to drink more alcoholic drinks. Although variety affects everyone, it affects extroverts most, and this is why they seek out foods that supply it.

Monotony

It is easy to forget that a monotonous diet is the rule in most cultures and that modern industrial societies are the great exception. Most cuisines are based around a staple carbohydrate (e.g. cassava, rice, pasta, potatoes, bread) and a distinctive taste mixture (e.g. chilli, oregano and tomato, curry spices). In most peasant economies the staple is the most reliable food to which others, such as meat, are added if and when they become available. As a Russian doctor observed in the 1880s when discussing the diet of Russian peasants: 'No one has any choice. Everyone, from young to old, must eat the same thing, and eat it day in and day out.' Or, as the historian Braudel remarked about the diet of pre-industrial Europe: 'Eating consisted of a lifetime of consuming bread, more bread, and still more bread.'

Spices were used to reduce monotony, and they were so valued that the search for them led Europeans to discover new continents and to circumnavigate the world. The people of Israel, led by Moses through Sinai on the path from Egypt, were provided with manna, a food of homogeneous composition to which they rapidly developed specific satiety. They compared it unfavourably with tasty foods such as leeks, onions, and garlic, and the fish, cucumber, and melons left behind in Egypt. (Modern research suggests that manna was a secretion produced by the larvae of insects that dwell on the tamarisk bush in that region. This fits the Biblical account of manna, because it is secreted at night. It has a light brown appearance and tastes like honey. Like Biblical manna it vanishes as the day goes on, not through decay but by being eaten by ants, which become more active as the day progresses and the soil warms.)

On monotonous diets foods that were appetising become less so. In the days of three-year voyages in sailing ships sailors survived mainly on preserved foods, which lost their appeal. When the craving for tasty foods such as onions was satisfied, it was documented as 'a glorious treat. We were perfectly ravenous for them. It was like the scent of blood to a hound.' Studies of the reactions of soldiers to a limited diet show that foods become less and less acceptable, and because of this, may even have adverse effects on nutrition. These adverse effects are seen most poignantly among people who have fled from famine areas in Africa to live in refugee camps where they are supplied with a more adequate, but still very restricted diet. A study recently carried out in a Sudanese refugee camp found that those who had been in the camp for six months found the foods provided to be much less pleasant than those who had been there only a short time (and were in a comparable state of health). There was even reason to think that, with the build-up of long-term specific satiety, people ceased preparing the foods properly, and suffered greater infection by parasites as a result.

Conclusions

We do have an instinct to eat what we need, but it usually has little effect, being submerged beneath much more powerful forces. Our capacity to learn, both from our experiences with foods and from wider social influences, gives rise to these dominant forces. We learn what to eat. The beliefs we acquire are probably the most important influence on our eating habits, but other factors, such as variety and the role of external cues, are extremely important, even though we may not be aware of them. Appetite is influenced by many factors, but psychological factors are most important; our minds determine what goes into our mouths.

What goes into our mouths also affects our emotions and behaviour. The next two chapters look at some of these influences, at the way our mouths affect our minds.

6

Mouth over mind: can the foods we eat make us mad or bad?

The effects of food on behaviour

People have always believed that the food they eat affects their actions and emotions. Whether or not they are right to believe this is a matter of controversy. In this chapter we will look at these issues, including claims that changes in diet can improve the behaviour of violent criminals, hyperactive children and the mentally ill.

All cultures have believed in the power of food. In the Middle Ages in Europe food was regarded as medicine that has clear effects on emotion and behaviour. In the fourteenth century the following two meals would have been expected to produce opposing emotional effects. The first is a salad composed of lettuce, rue and purslane, followed by *vinum satrinum*, a perfumed yellow wine. The second is rare roast beef cooked in saffron-flavoured pastry, and served with turnips, and with leeks cooked with honey, sesame and almonds.

Both meals were thought to affect sexual desire, the second meal in a positive direction, and the first in a negative direction

– it was in fact called 'Abstinence Salad'. In the same period those with a tendency to depression were advised to avoid fried meat and highly salted foods and to eat boiled meat, cows' milk and egg yolks. The opposite view was taken by the seventeenth-century writer Robert Burton who, in his *Anatomy of Melancholy*, cited milk as a cause of depression. 'Milk and all that comes of milk, as butter and cheese, curds . . . increases melancholy.' Sydney Smith, the Georgian essayist, who characterised Heaven as eating 'pâtés de foie gras to the sound of trumpets', and Hell as 'a thousand years of tough mutton', also had views on the effects of foods. He believed in the character-building properties of beef, mutton, pie crust and rich soups, and the depressing effects of toasted cheese, lobster, and hard salted meat. The great early nineteenth-century Shakespearian actor Edmund Kean used food to help him prepare for performances. Before playing the part of a tyrant he would eat pork, before acting as a lover he would eat mutton, and before adopting the role of a murderer he would dine on beef. In this century Mahatma Gandhi believed that abstaining from meat and milk would enable him to overcome his 'animal desires'.

Today a great deal is written about the effects of food on behaviour. A best-selling book, *Why your child is hyperactive*, blames food additives for this disorder. Another best-seller, *Not all in the mind*, claims that food allergy is a major cause of mental illness. There are claims that 'junk food' contributes to crime. What should we make of these books and claims? Should we pay them any respect or should we view them with the same incredulity as we view Abstinence Salad and Burton's views? Powerful claims are made on both sides, usually in the absence of firm evidence. How should we make up our minds? Books such as those cited contain persuasive case studies, showing near-miraculous improvements in individuals. Are these convincing enough? Because this is such a controversial area we shall consider how to evaluate such claims before looking in detail at the claims themselves.

The Prince of Wales's diet

In 1858, Queen Victoria was worried about her seventeen-year-old son, the Prince of Wales, who subsequently became Edward VII. He seemed incapable of learning much, despite having individual tutors, he had a strong sense of inferiority, and occasionally behaved badly in adult company, interrupting conversations, picking bad-tempered arguments, and occasionally screaming his head off in tantrums. When he was eleven his tutor described him as 'extremely disobedient, impertinent to his masters, and unwilling to be disciplined', and reported that he was unable to 'play at any game for five minutes, or attempt anything new or difficult without losing his temper'. The Queen's physician, Sir James Clark, recommended a new diet (listed below) to cure the Prince of these ills.

The Prince of Wales's diet

Breakfast	*9 am*	*bread and butter*
		one egg
		tea, coffee or cocoa
Lunch	*2 pm*	*meat and vegetables*
		no pudding
		seltzerwater
Dinner	*7 pm*	*a light meal of meat and vegetables*
		claret and seltzer water (in hot weather)
		sherry and water (in cold weather)
		no coffee
Late night	*9 pm*	*a cup of tea*

There were signs of general improvement a year later, although the teenage Prince was still impulsive, shallow and distractible. Was this because of the diet? Or was it because of other changes in his life that occurred during that year? His rather rigid tutor departed, and he was able to enjoy a much freer way of life. It is very difficult to say with certainty that changes in a person's diet are responsible for changes in behaviour. In this case the diet was not the only way in which

99

Edward's parents were trying to influence his behaviour; they also tried a range of approaches, including appointing a 'Governor' to be responsible for him, and arranging for him to spend periods at Oxford University and Cambridge University. He was also gradually maturing, and it is possible that his behaviour may have improved merely with the passage of time, diet or no diet. Another difficulty in attributing the improvements in his behaviour to his diet is that no very strict check was kept on what he actually ate. It is quite possible that the teenage Prince managed to acquire whatever food he wanted, despite the diet, or indeed, as part of a reaction against it.

A final reason for scepticism about Clark's diet for the Prince lies in how its results (i.e. the changes in his behaviour) were evaluated. The changes were assessed from the observations of the very people who had initially complained of his behaviour, sought help for it, and implemented this help (i.e. Queen Victoria and Prince Albert). How accurate and reliable were their observations and judgements? It is interesting that, as Edward apparently improved in his behaviour, he spent less and less time with his parents, and it is possible that his behaviour was not actually generally better, but that he made an effort when he was with them. Albert and Victoria's judgement might also have been affected by their faith in the competence of Sir James Clark (he had attended Victoria as a child, and she had appointed him as her physician on her first day as monarch); they could have 'seen' improvements where none occurred.

These difficulties in interpreting the effectiveness of Clark's diet for the Prince do not just apply to that particular example, but are issues which arise in any attempt to evaluate the effects on behaviour of dietary change. It is useful to begin by considering these issues precisely because the topic is so controversial. We can summarise each of these methodological points as questions to be addressed to any study, together with ways of overcoming each problem (see Table 4).

Table 4   How to check the claims of diets

	questions	solutions
1	Are the effects due to just the passing of time? Would they have occurred anyway, diet or no diet?	Compare people who have the diet with others who do not (a 'control group'). Are the changes in the diet group greater than those in the control group?
2	Is the dietary change actually made? Do the people on the diet actually follow it?	Control and record the food that those in both groups actually eat. Ideally supply all food to all people in the study.
3	Is behaviour assessed before and after the dietary change?	Assess several aspects of behaviour as objectively as possible.
4	Are the assessments made by persons who know which person is getting what treatment?	Remove any possible bias by preventing the people doing the assessment from knowing which person is on which diet, so that they are 'blind' assessors.
5	Do the subjects of the experiment know what is happening?	Use 'blind' subjects (who do not know the purpose of the diet they are on). In the most objective studies ('double blind' studies) neither the subjects nor the assessors are in the know.
6	Are subjects randomly allocated to treatments and controls?	People who could take part in the study are allocated to either the treatment diet or the control diet randomly, by chance.

Thus, to eliminate bias, and find out how helpful Clark's diet is for teenage boys with learning difficulties, it would be necessary to study a group of such boys (say forty of them). At random half would be chosen to receive the Prince of Wales's diet and half to eat a 'normal' diet; the boys would not know which group they were in. They would all have their learning ability measured before and after by psychologists who had no knowledge of the study. Trained 'blind' observers would observe the boys' social behaviour with adults to rate the frequency of such manifestations as screaming etc. The boys would all be supplied with meals and supervised to see that they ate these and nothing else. This would be the simplest type of research necessary to establish the effects of the diet. Anything less would not do.

Scientific rigour is required because, unlike Queen Victoria, most psychologists and doctors are highly sceptical of claims that diet affects behaviour. Because of this views tend to be polarised between 'conventional' professionals who don't even deem the topic worthy of debate, and 'believers' who enthusiastically put forward their views, mainly to other 'believers'. The unfortunate thing about this polarisation is that it diverts attention away from a sober scientific evaluation of the claims of both parties. What matters most of all is to find out what truth, if any, lies in these claims. Many important new ideas in science arose from people who at the time were regarded as 'cranks' or unconventional; being seen as a 'crank' is no guarantee that a person's views are incorrect (or, indeed, correct!).

Interestingly enough, there are several parallels between the case of the Prince of Wales and modern controversies. One of the disorders for which dietary treatment has been recommended is hyperactivity, a disorder which shows itself in concentration difficulties, learning problems, impulsivity etc. – all problems the young Edward VII displayed. When hyperactive boys grow up into adults they often continue to show residual problems of impulsiveness, antisocial behaviour and lack of concentration. It is an open question whether the Prince's career as King of England was successful or not! During his time as Prince of Wales Edward was able to enjoy pleasures that might have resulted in imprisonment for a less privileged person and throughout his life he had a fiery temper and would never have been described as an intellectual.

The doctor who had prescribed the diet, James Clark, was an able, open-minded, and widely travelled doctor (who had attended Keats in Rome, and carried out research into the temperature of the Gulf Stream). His medical views were not restricted to those of his conventional colleagues, so that, for example, he had great enthusiasm for fresh air. Believing that the atmosphere of Buckingham Palace was saturated with moisture from the many nearby trees, he had wanted to have a machine pump fresh air into the Palace. He was quick to see the value of chloroform for pain relief in childbirth (a highly controversial issue at the time) and, under his guidance, Victoria had this for the delivery of Prince Leopold, her eighth child, in 1853, thus popularising the drug among her subjects. The nature of the diet recommended for the young Prince is not, as we shall see, one that has been recently recommended for hyperactive children, except that it would (like most foods at that time) be free from the artificial flavourings and preservatives that are blamed for many behaviour problems in children.

Although many different claims have been made for the effects of diet on behaviour, in this chapter we shall focus on the three main areas where research has been carried out – hyperactivity, criminality and mental illness.

Hyperactivity and Diet

'Hyperactivity' is a childhood behaviour disorder character-ised by hyperactive (over-active) behaviour, poor concent-ration and attention, and impulsivity. Examples of hyperactive behaviour include excessively running around and climbing on things and finding it difficult to sit still. A hyperactive child is easily distracted, usually fails to finish things it has started, and often seems not to listen to parents and teachers. Signs of impulsivity include finding it difficult to organise work, frequently acting before thinking, and frequently calling out in class. Hyperactivity is mainly diagnosed in boys (three times as often as in girls), most frequently at eight years of age. In extreme cases the diagnosis is clear, with parents having great difficulty coping with a boy rushing around from one activity to another, not persisting for long at anything, always 'on the go', disobedient at home and at school, with poor relationships with other children. Not surprisingly, such children do poorly in their academic work at school. In less extreme cases the diagnosis is more difficult; many children show mild versions of these features and none of them is unique to hyperactivity. The diagnosis is made more often in the USA than in the UK, probably because of different diagnostic criteria rather than because hyperactivity is more common there. In the UK fewer than one per cent of children are diagnosed as hyperactive; in the USA (where it is the most common problem referred to child psychiatrists) about seven per cent are. Hyperactive children have an excessive number of medical problems just before or after birth and most have a difficult temperament from infancy.

What happens to hyperactive children as they grow up?

When studies of hyperactive children are followed up in later years when the children have grown up, much of the hyperactive behaviour has disappeared but there is still a very strong tendency for them to show a great deal of antisocial behaviour, and problems associated with impulsivity such as excessive anger or the abuse of alcohol or other drugs. They have poor relationships with others of their age and a rather negative view of themselves. The concentration problems evident in childhood tend to persist into adulthood, so that their educational attainments are lower than those of adults of similar intellectual level. The problems of hyperactive children persist into adulthood.

The treatment of hyperactivity

The main conventional forms of treatment for this disorder are drugs and behaviour therapy. Paradoxical though it may seem, drug treatment involves the use of stimulant drugs (such as the amphetamines or methylphenidate), which increase the level of activity in the brain rather than sedatives, which reduce it. This is because hyperactive children appear to have an underactive brain that is hungry for stimulation; excessive physical activity stimulates the brain and satisfies this hunger. Stimulant drugs directly increase brain activity, and have been found to produce beneficial changes in many sufferers. In the USA drug treatment is widely used and about one child in thirty is on medication for this problem; in the UK it is much less used. Many people are concerned about long-term medication for hyperactive children, because there is evidence that it can have undesirable side-effects such as sleep disturbance, and the suppression of normal growth. It also becomes less and less effective over a period of months, and is incapable of producing improvements in school performance.

Behaviour therapy for hyperactivity has involved the systematic use of immediate rewards for positive or constructive behaviour which is incompatible with some aspects of the disorder. An example would be immediately rewarding hyperactive children in class whenever they attend to their tasks. At first they are rewarded (with praise, a sweet, or a token, which can later be cashed in for something the child likes) whenever they spend any time engaged in their work. As they start to do this more the rewards are only given for attending to work for short periods of time, and the length of the period is gradually increased as improvements occur. The standard is gradually 'upped'. In addition to this conditioning approach there is 'self-instructional training' in which hyperactive children are taught to restrain their behaviour by talking to themselves in helpful ways, at first aloud, then by whispering, and then silently. In this way they learn to consciously inhibit excessive behaviour and to direct their attention towards what they should be doing. A distractible child might learn to say to himself: 'I'm just wandering off what I'm supposed to be doing. What should I be doing now? Let's see. . . .' Both of those behaviour therapy approaches can be very useful for some children, but neither is effective for all. They are essentially ways of managing some components of the disorder rather than changing the temperament of the child.

105

Conventional medical and psychological treatments have been unable to provide a very adequate solution to the problems posed by hyperactive children. It is therefore important to seriously consider other treatment approaches, and the most important of these have been dietary treatments. Hyperactivity has been attributed to a sensitivity to certain types of constituents of foods, or to an allergic response to foods.

The Feingold hypothesis

The first clear suggestion about the role of diet in hyper-activity came from Ben Feingold, an American doctor specialising in allergy at the Kaiser-Permanante Hospital in California. From his observations of many children suffering from allergies he initially formed the impression that hyper-active children are extra-sensitive to aspirin (acetylsalicylic acid); he thought that their behaviour could be aggravated by ingesting this or foods which naturally contain its close relatives, the salicylates. Feingold suggested that eliminating such foods (listed in Table 5) from the child's diet would reduce hyperactivity.

Table 5   Foods containing natural salicylates

almonds	currants	pineapple
apples	french beans	prunes
apricots	gooseberries	plums
blackberries	grapes	raisins
cherries	mint flavours	raspberries
cloves	nectarines	strawberries
corn on the cob	oranges	tea
cucumbers and pickles	peaches	tomatoes

Feingold later added artificial food additives to the list of suspect substances because patients who are sensitive to aspirin are often also sensitive to tartrazine, a commonly used orange food dye. Tartrazine-sensitive persons also tend to be sensitive to aspirin, although there are few chemical similarities between the two substances. Feingold pointed out that the use of such artificial chemicals as food dyes, flavours and preservatives has developed over the same years as hyperactivity has apparently become more widespread. Since 1939 the amount of such substances in Western diets has increased tenfold. He suggested that this was no coincidence, but that many of these food additives aggravate or produce hyperactivity in children disposed in that direction. His hypothesis (the 'Feingold hypothesis'), that the elimination from the diet of artificial additives, aspirin, and foods containing naturally occurring salicylates should reduce hyperactivity led to the production of such a diet.

This Kaiser-Permanante (or K–P) diet was described in his best-selling book *Why your child is hyperactive* (published in 1978). Feingold claimed that thirty to fifty per cent of afflicted children responded to this dietary treatment, and age was crucial, with younger children benefiting most. Children as young as three or five would be expected to improve completely within a few days on the K–P diet, while teenagers might take weeks and improve only partially. Feingold claimed that the first improvements were in the area of hyperactive, aggressive and impulsive behaviour, while improvements in co-ordination took longer, and improvements in attention and intellectual functioning were the last to occur. Feingold claimed that hyperactive, aggressive and impulsive behaviour could be 'turned on and off' fairly rapidly by dietary changes. Since conventional treatments were neither very effective nor risk-free, the claims for this relatively harmless dietary treatment were taken up enthusiastically by the parents of hyperactive children in the USA. Many 'Feingold Societies' grew up spontaneously to promote these views.

Was Feingold correct?

At first the only evidence for evaluating this treatment came from descriptions by Feingold and other enthusiasts of the response of patients whom they treated in this way. These were generally good and consistent with his claims. However they are not sufficient to allow a judgement as to whether the treatment worked, for the reasons outlined above in a discussion of the Prince of Wales's diet. During the next decade a series of much more adequate studies was carried out and results were published by many other researchers.

Some of these fulfilled many of the recommendations listed in Table 3. For example in one study carried out by Harley and co-workers at the University of Wisconsin and published in 1978 the researchers went to great lengths to test the hypothesis fairly and without bias. They compared the effects on the behaviour of hyperactive children for an equal period on the K–P diet and on a control diet; all children received both diets, half had the K–P diet first, and then the control diet, while the others had them in the reverse order. The researchers provided all food for the families to eat at home and for the children to eat at school. Precautions were taken to prevent the parents from identifying which diet the child was on at any one time, partly by misleading them as to which foods contained additives and which were additive-free. The children's behaviour was rated daily by the parents and teachers (who were also 'blind' to the treatment conditions) and the children were also observed by researchers in the classroom and received regular psychological testing (of concentration etc.) in the laboratory by blind assessors.

What were the results of this study? The Feingold hypothesis predicted that behaviour on the K–P diet would be much better than on the control diet. The results were fairly mixed. There was not the clear response that Feingold had claimed and no overall superiority of the K–P diet emerged. Therefore there was no clear support for the hypothesis. However, the K–P diet did better in parents' ratings for pre-school children, though not for those at school. Although this could be merely a chance finding it could also be interpreted as showing that the diet does have a mild effect on younger children, whom Feingold suggested should benefit most. A similar pattern of results emerged from other methodologically adequate treatment trials of the K–P diet; the strong claims were not supported, but there were suggestions that a small number of children derived some benefit from it.

Feingold's views were also tested by looking at the effects of giving hyperactive children food additives (so-called 'challenge studies'.) A series of challenge studies took the form of presenting children with cookies which either did or did not contain additives. To aid these trials the Nutrition Foundation in the USA provided the cookies. Again the results of adequate double-blind trials failed to support Feingold's strong claims, but suggested that a minority of hyperactive children were adversely affected by consuming additives. The major criticism of these challenge studies is that they failed to test the children sufficiently – the cookies contained much smaller amounts of dye than the children habitually consumed. Originally the amount in the cookies supplied to researchers by the Nutrition Foundation was based on the results of a survey that suggested the average American consumed 26 mg of additives a day. However, it has since become clear that children consume more than this (the daily average for five-to-twelve-year-olds is 57 mg) and that hyperactive children consume much more dye than the average child; many consume more than 150 mg a day. Therefore negative findings from challenge studies which presented low (less than 50 mg) doses of dye cannot be conclusive. Further studies employing larger doses (100 mg) have found limited effects on learning ability but not on general behaviour.

What, then, can we conclude about Feingold's hypothesis? His claims that fifty per cent of children would benefit from the K–P diet have found little support; it is not a dramatic cure for hyperactivity. There appears to be a minority of children who benefit in limited ways, but they can only be identified from their response to the diet and not in any other way. The dramatic improvements in patients reported by Feingold and other workers are largely due to factors other than dietary treatment.

Hyperactivity and food allergy

Feingold focused interest on the role of diet in hyperactivity, but proposed only one way in which food can affect behaviour. Another possibility – of food allergy – has been proposed in recent years. This is a wider suggestion, since it has been implied that the sufferer can be allergic to one of many substances. Testing it therefore requires individualised investigation to find which food the child is allergic to, before setting up a treatment regime. As we shall see it is ironic that, in contrast to Feingold's indictment of artificial food additives, most of the foodstuffs implicated in food allergies are entirely natural substances such as cows' milk, meat and wheat.

What is food allergy?

Food allergies differ from food sensitivities because, unlike them, they involve disorders in the body's immune system. True allergic responses develop within a few hours of exposure to the food but can last for several days. They are caused by cells called mast cells (after the German *mast* meaning fat), which are bloated with chemicals capable of causing the allergic response. Contact with the allergen causes the mast cells to shed their load of allergy-producing chemicals and thus provoke familiar allergic reactions. The classical and well recognised effects of allergies include asthma, urticaria (hives), tingling in the lips, mouth or throat, sneezing or a blocked nose, and pain or bloating in the stomach or diarrhoea. Bonny Prince Charlie suffered from an allergy to milk which took the form of diarrhoea; when he drank only water this disappeared.

The controversial issue is whether food allergy can aggravate hyperactivity. There are several reasons for thinking that it might. Firstly, studies of hyperactive children by specialists in allergy have found them to display many allergic responses to foods, with more food allergies in the more severely hyperactive children. Secondly, children suffering from 'classical' food allergies who are treated by a diet excluding the

110

offending items have shown marked improvements in their
behaviour. Thirdly, and most convincingly, a double-blind
trial has shown that such an exclusion diet markedly improves
behaviour.

Only one such study has been published to date, carried out
by Joseph Egger and his colleagues at Great Ormond Street
Hospital for Sick Children in London. Initially seventy-six
hyperactive children were placed on a fairly restricted
nutritious diet which contained no substances commonly
associated with allergies. The behaviour of sixty-two of them
improved while on the diet (twenty-one improved completely), and they underwent a further period of testing in
which they stayed on the diet but had a 'new' food introduced
each week. If behaviour worsened the food was withdrawn,
otherwise it became a regular part of the diet. Where foods
containing artificial dyes or flavourings (e.g. orange squash)
provoked a response, the child was tested with capsules of the
additive (e.g. tartrazine E102). Those children who were thus
shown to respond to particular foods entered a double blind
trial. In this they were exposed to the food to which they had
reacted and also to a placebo food which they found difficult to
distinguish from it. Thus, for example, instead of cows' milk
the child might have soya milk, sheep's milk, or goats' milk;
some foods (both suspect and placebo) were presented sealed
in cans by a food manufacturer. The parents and the doctor
were blind to the nature of the foods.

The results showed clear improvements on the placebo
foods, and worsening on the suspect foods (on ratings made
by doctors, a psychologist and parents). The commonest
substances aggravating behaviour were the dye tartrazine
(E102) and the preservative benzoic acid (E210) – but no child
reacted badly to these alone. The next most common 'suspect'
foods were natural ones – cows' milk, and then wheat, eggs,
oranges and chocolate. Three-quarters of the children
improved with dietary treatment, and one third of the children
recovered almost completely. Interestingly, children with
stressful family or social backgrounds reacted much less

clearly than others; it appears that dietary and social factors act together. This study is the firmest evidence we have that food allergy can aggravate hyperactivity. It is ironic that the results implicate so many natural foods as allergens; if these substances are generally important in aggravating hyperactivity it would make it hard to accept Feingold's claims that the use of artificial additives has caused an increase in the incidence of this disorder.

Some hyperactive children clearly benefit from dietary treatment, although it may only be possible to identify these responders from a trial on a diet such as that used in the study described above by Egger. Claims that as many as half of hyperactive children would benefit may overestimate the effectiveness of dietary treatments, though since other treatments for hyperactivity are not much more effective and – in the case of drugs – may have unwanted side-effects, trying children on a dietary regime to assess their response will be attractive to many parents.

Diet and antisocial behaviour

If hyperactive children can benefit from dietary treatment, then why not young offenders? The problems of many hyperactive children persist into adulthood and can bring them into conflict with society and the law. It is possible that these behaviour problems can be affected by diet. Explorations of dietary treatments of hyperactivity suggest that younger children respond most rapidly and completely. Is it too late by adolescence and early adulthood? A group of American workers has produced evidence that it is not, and their challenging results may force us to have to rethink our views on antisocial behaviour.

Crime and antisocial behaviour have been increasing for several decades and no generally effective method of prevention or of rehabilitating offenders has been established. Locking up offenders in prison protects us from their behaviour while they are there, but has no effect on their behaviour after they are released; prisons often teach their inmates a wider repertoire of criminal habits. Any positive approach is worth considering seriously.

Prison studies in the USA

The American sociologist Stephen Schoenthaler has reported the effects of improving the diet in twelve institutions for young offenders, involving 6,084 offenders in American States from Alabama to California. The overall result has been to halve the amount of antisocial behaviour observed within the institutions, including violence and suicide attempts.

What were the changes in diet? How were the changes in behaviour measured? How adequate are the studies? The dietary changes, listed below in Table 6, were intended to reduce the amount of sugar (sucrose) and fats consumed.

Table 6   Dietary changes in Schoenthaler's studies

1	Breakfast cereals without added sugars replaced those with sugar.
2	Tinned fruits packed in syrup were rinsed in cold water before being served.
3	Soft drinks were replaced with a wide variety of fruit juices, and machines dispensing soft drinks were replaced with those dispensing fruit juices.
4	Iced tea was served unsweetened.
5	Bowls of sugar on the table were replaced with bowls of honey.
6	Wholewheat bread replaced refined white bread.
7	Brown rice replaced white rice.
8	As far as possible processed foods were replaced with fresh produce.
9	'Junk' snack foods (high in sugar and/or fat) were replaced with more nutritious equivalents. Ice creams, sweets, cakes, crisps, etc. were forbidden and were replaced with fresh fruits, vegetables, nuts, cheeses, wholegrain snacks etc.
10	Parents were asked not to send foods incompatible with the diet.

These changes are in line with health educators' recommendations to reduce the amount of sugar and fat and increase the amount of fibre in the diet. The only odd change is the substitution of honey for sugar – it contains just as much energy; the rationale was that less would be taken to sweeten drinks. It is relatively easy to produce consistent changes in diet in closed institutions such as those studied by Schoenthaler, although visitors can smuggle in foods forbidden on the diet.

Schoenthaler carried out five studies into the effects of making these changes to the diet in different correctional institutions, involving 5,603 inmates. In each there was a clear drop in the frequency of antisocial acts of between twenty-one and forty-eight per cent. In some cases it was possible to look at the kinds of improvements in behaviour seen within the institution. For example, one study of 3,399 offenders in North California found that during the new dietary regime there were hardly any improvements in disobedience, verbal abuse, or smuggling contraband into the institution. However there were large improvements in the frequency of physical assaults (a twenty-five per cent drop), disruptions (a forty-two per cent drop) and suicide attempts (none occurred).

A sixth study (in Fairfax County Virginia) took a different form. Instead of changing the diet by substituting healthier alternatives a nutritious food, fresh orange juice, was added to the diet. On each table at mealtimes jugs of milk and water were normally available for the residents to drink as they wished; the only change made for the study was the addition of a third pitcher, of orange juice. The study was double-blind; only two administrators of the system knew of the study; the offenders and staff were unaware of it. This is therefore the only really adequate study of the six projects and its conclusions (a forty-one per cent drop in antisocial behaviour) need to be taken seriously. The results of the other five studies challenge conventional views and need to be replicated by other workers and tested more rigorously under double-blind conditions to assess behaviour change in a more detailed and objective way. None of the six studies measures up to all of the scientific standards set out in Table 3; until researchers employ the highest standards their results can only be suggestive rather than definitive.

Why should these relatively simple dietary changes produce such significant changes in behaviour? The purpose of the first five diets was to reduce the intake of sugar (sucrose) and the amount of artificial food additives, and to increase the intake of more nutritious foods. Many professionals have indicted sugar as having an aggravating role in behaviour for some individuals, especially if combined with additives. The role of additives in hyperactive children (many of whom grow up to become offenders) has already been discussed. There are also many suggestions that the diet of offenders may be seriously lacking nutritionally. The American psychologist Alexander Schauss has collected evidence which reveals that many offenders have very poor diets, largely composed of 'junk foods' (processed foods containing calories and additives but few nutrients). These can cause 'overconsumption malnutrition', an excess of energy combined with borderline subclinical shortages of nutrients such as vitamins and minerals, which are required for essential brain functions. In a state of overconsumption malnutrition youngsters can suffer from deficiencies in minerals such as iron, and there is a link between mineral deficiencies and lack of concentration, conduct disorders etc. Such young people, it is argued, are particularly sensitive to stress, and the combination of under-nutrition, a diet rich in sugar and additives, and social stress combine to aggravate any impulsivity or antisocial tendencies. It follows that young offenders may benefit from a healthy diet, which will restore nutritional balance and detoxify the system of additives. These suggestions (and others) would need to be tested carefully if Schoenthaler's results were replicated elsewhere by other workers using better experimental methods (double-blind studies, direct observations of behaviour, placebo changes in diet etc.).

Schoenthaler's results are challenging because they imply that simple, benign dietary changes can improve the behaviour of incarcerated offenders, which is a very difficult thing to do. They need to be taken seriously and the studies replicated elsewhere in a more rigorous manner. If the beneficial results are repeated then it would be necessary to begin to look at why the diet works, or which dietary changes are of most benefit. Until then constructive scepticism may be the best attitude to adopt.

Diet and mental illness

Food has also been blamed for mental illness. During the last two decades some psychiatrists and allergists have claimed that sensitivities to particular foods can cause or aggravate a range of serious mental illnesses and emotional disorders in adults. This view has been popularised by books such as *Not all in the mind* by a British psychiatrist, Richard Mackarness. There are many persuasive accounts of patients whose problems failed to respond to the full range of conventional treatments but were then successfully treated by dietary approaches. The implication has been drawn that many other patients might benefit from such approaches and that much mental illness might be caused by sensitivities or allergies to foods. These views are highly controversial, as can be seen from the furious row that arose within the pages of a British psychological journal after one psychologist claimed that ninety per cent of neurotic patients could benefit from dietary treatment. The depth of feeling aroused by this controversy was extraordinary, and led to the possibility of legal action. Out of these controversial views, a new discipline, 'clinical ecology', has developed. Clinical ecologists specialise in assessing the involvement of foods (and other substances, such as aerosol sprays) in disorders and in providing treatments where they are involved. Clinical ecology has been viewed with suspicion by conventional psychology and medicine because it claims so much, and it has remained a fringe discipline. A consequence is that, in Britain at least, many clinical ecologists practise in the private system outside the NHS; it is hard for the patient to distinguish between highly professional clinical ecologists and unscrupulous persons who exploit patients for gain.

What is important is the truth or falsity of the claim that food causes mental disorders. If dietary therapies are proven to be effective, then they would be a welcome addition to the range of treatments available. The reasons why they work (if they do) are a secondary issue; many effective treatments for emotional disorders – such as ECT, hypnosis, and some drugs – are used because they work and despite the fact that why they work is still a mystery. In the eighteenth century the British Navy adopted the policy of having sailors eat limes (hence they were called 'Limeys') in order to prevent scurvy, even though it was not until 1912 that Hopkins discovered that scurvy is caused by a deficiency in vitamin C, which limes contain. The fact that we do not have a satisfactory explanation of how dietary treatments could cure mental disorders should not prevent us from considering the issue of whether they could – if psychiatrists used only drugs whose mode of action was well understood they would use very few! The need for rigorous scientific appraisal is essential, especially as the power of suggestion is so great in this area. Unfortunately there are far more ideas and claims than there are scientific studies.

Evidence

One investigation into the possibility of food allergy as a cause of psychiatric disorder was carried out in an allergy clinic in Manchester. Patients attending because of emotional disorders had a thorough medical and psychiatric assessment. Their reactions to food were examined by a process similar to that employed in Egger's study of hyperactive children. They first went on a restricted diet free from common allergens (and based on lamb, rice and pears); after a while they sampled foods that seemed likely to provoke a response until the culprits were identified after having been sampled on several occasions. The patients were subjected to a double-blind challenge test to three foods and three placebo substances, presented in either capsules or drinks. In this way it was possible to identify which foods they reacted to when they were unaware of what they were consuming; allergic reactions are purely physical and occur independently of conscious awareness.

The results were very clear. Only seventeen per cent of patients showed reliable reactions to foods during double-blind testing. Others showed just as many and as intense bad reactions but these occurred just as often with placebos as with 'problem foods'. The responders to food were different from the others in two ways. Firstly, their reactions to 'suspect' foods were the classical allergic responses (e.g. rhinitis, urticaria, asthma and eczema); none of the others reacted in this way. The non-responders complained of a wide range of other symptoms, including lethargy, head pains, depression, palpitations and mood swings. Secondly, the responders showed little psychiatric disorder, unlike the non-responders, who all showed emotional distress. In fact the non-responders showed as many psychological problems as a series of consecutive new outpatients at a local psychiatric clinic (they only differed from these by tending to come from higher social classes). The responders had classical food allergies when faced with 'problem foods', but no psychiatric disorder; the non-responders responded to 'problem foods' with a range of psychological symptoms, and also suffered from psychiatric disorder.

When told about the results of the double-blind tests half of the non-responders accepted that they did not suffer from food allergy and improved rapidly. Only a few of the non-responders who persisted in their belief that a food allergy was the cause of their symptoms eventually improved, and this was with the aid of antidepressant medication or a move to a less stressful job. These patients in particular and, to some extent, most of the attenders at the Allergy Clinic were hostile to suggestions that their symptoms might have a psychological rather than a physical cause. They were so similar to psychiatric patients that the only reason they had been referred to an allergist rather than a psychiatrist was that they would have refused to see a psychiatrist. The suggestion that a psychiatrist could help was often interpreted as meaning that the patient's symptoms were imaginary rather than real. To have a 'medical' problem such as a food allergy was seen as more acceptable than to have a psychological problem. The same is even more true for hyperactivity – 'it's his food allergy' is a less threatening explanation for a child's behaviour than 'it's the way I've brought him up'! In fact a psychological disorder such as depression is probably better news than a food allergy because it can often be successfully treated, whereas food allergy implies a restricted diet for life.

These results indicate that many people who believe that their symptoms are due to food allergy are mistaken, and that the intensity of their symptoms when they knowingly eat 'problem foods' is no guide as to whether or not they are mistaken. Only double-blind testing can settle the issue in any particular person. More studies like this are necessary to assess what proportion (if any) of psychiatric disorders are caused by food intolerance and respond to dietary treatments. Enthusiastic case studies are not enough, but are about all we have to go on at present. The issue should be taken seriously and studied further, but at present no firm conclusions can be reached.

The psychology of food intolerance

Many adverse reactions to foods (and other substances) can be purely psychological in origin or they can result from a combination of organic and psychological causes. They are none the less real (and painful) for being psychological and are equally deserving of help. But, as hinted above, many sufferers prefer to attribute their symptoms to 'physical' disorders for which they hope to find 'physical' cures, rather than to admit to psychological problems. A rare but dramatic illustration of this is the 'total allergy syndrome', in which sufferers refuse to eat, complain of a variety of symptoms, and fly to the USA for expensive treatments. This disorder, which few allergists accept as an allergic response, has many similarities to the eating disorder anorexia nervosa (considered in Chapter 10). It mainly affects young females, sufferers experience a drop in weight and stop eating, etc.; the only difference is that sufferers of 'total allergy syndrome' explain their behaviour as an allergy, but anorexics explain theirs as an attempt to prevent fatness. Both disorders have psychological causes; sufferers of the first disorder refuse to acknowledge this.

The position with child disorders is even more complex. If a mother believes that her child's bad behaviour is due to food preservatives, she can (unconsciously) 'train' her child to behave accordingly. One of the author's colleagues tells how at a children's party, the mother of one boy told other mothers that if her son drank the orange squash he would 'become hyperactive' and proceeded to give him a glass saying to everyone: 'You just watch him now, he'll go wild!' Whether or not he responded to the squash he was very likely to have responded to her prompting and to have enjoyed her 'permission' to misbehave. The involvement of adults also raises the issue of what happens if a food-sensitive child does abstain from the harmful substance. Do the family's patterns of reactions to that child's habitual behaviour vanish rapidly, or do they, like most habits, take time to change, and continue to produce the bad behaviour? Is this one reason for practitioners such as Feingold reporting that the older a child is the less complete the response to dietary treatment?

If hyperactivity is discovered to be food-linked, there may still be a problem with the patient's attitude towards the culprit food. The difficulties of reducing consumption of alcohol or of sticking to a diet show that mere knowledge of what is bad for us is not enough! Many clinicians have observed that, for example, hyperactive children can show strong preferences for the very foods that cause the problems. This could be because the consequences of eating them (e.g. disinhibited behaviour) are in some sense rewarding to the child (as the effects of alcohol can be to adult drinkers). Or it could be that some degree of adaptation to or tolerance of the dangerous food has occurred, so that withdrawal symptoms follow if it is omitted from the diet, and a pleasant feeling ensues when consumption is resumed. This can certainly happen with coffee in individuals particularly sensitive to it. These are merely suggestions, and as yet we have no firm reasons for understanding why people eat foods that cause them to suffer.

Conclusion

There is little doubt that what we eat can effect how we act. Whether this is because of what is in the food or because of what we believe about the food has yet to be settled and, in different cases, one or both of these factors may operate. We will be able to judge only when further evidence comes to light; the research is incomplete and the topic one of controversy. If dietary treatments are found to be effective, the implications for how we deal with many problems will be tremendous; dietary treatments are frequently cheap and more benign than their alternatives.

Our eating habits are also bound up with many other areas of our lives, which are less exciting, but apply to all of us, rather than to just the small number of people who become criminals or mentally ill. The next chapter looks at two of those areas, sleep and character.

7

Eating habits affect sleeping habits and help form character

Our eating habits are bound up with many aspects of life. In this chapter we look at the connections between eating and sleeping, and at the claims that early eating habits form character.

Sleeping and eating are two activities that are so common as to be 'invisible' to us. They are also intimately linked together and intertwined. From birth the two activities alternate and are the main occupations of the young infant. They gradually become disengaged as the child grows, but still influence one another in many ways.

The sleep cycle

Only a stranger from another planet would think to stop and ask why humans cease all activity and retire to bed for a third of their lives; we are so used to it that it doesn't strike us as extraordinary. Yet different species sleep for different amounts of time; the giraffe hardly ever closes its eyes, while the bush baby is hardly ever awake. Why should humans sleep for seven or eight hours in every twenty-four hours? While asleep we are rarely still for long, either mentally or physically. After falling asleep our bodies and minds gradually become more and more relaxed and less and less active. Our muscles become more and more limp and pliable, our heart rate goes down and down, our body temperature and blood pressure drop, and our brain activity slows down. Eventually we reach a stage of sleep ('slow wave sleep') in which the body is completely relaxed; if we woke up then, our minds would most likely be empty.

The nature of sleep then changes dramatically; the body becomes much more active – our eyes move from side to side as if looking at something, although we do not blink, and our heart beats much faster. Yet all this activity is deceptive because we are no more awake than before, in fact it may take much louder noises to wake us up, and on awakening we would report that we had been dreaming. In this kind of dreaming sleep – called REM sleep ('rapid eye movement sleep') because of the rapid eye movements which are so striking to observers – the mind and body can be far more active than when we are awake. The brain is highly active, pulsing with rapid waves of electrical activity. The sexual organs become aroused for a time, whatever we are dreaming about, whether or not our dreams are erotic. Suddenly all this activity ends and we come back up almost to consciousness, to a very shallow level of sleep; then we begin the process all over again by starting to drift down to slow wave sleep. At various points in this process our bodies become very active and we thrash about. The cycle takes about one and a half hours to complete and occurs about five times in any one night. On average we dream for about one and a half hours a night, although we may not remember anything about it in the morning. It is astonishing that most people do not remember their most exciting experiences each day, their dreams. Sleeping is so different from the rest of our lives, yet we rarely give it much thought.

Apart from the fact that being asleep is the only activity which is incompatible with feeding, sleep being our main fasting period, how are sleep and eating intertwined? They are both influenced by body rhythms, and in infancy these develop together; in adult life they influence one another. The foods we eat influence the quality and quantity of our sleep, because of their action on the brain.

The sleep cycle is a very obvious body rhythm, but it is not the only one. It is part of a rhythmic variation in alertness that occurs over the whole twenty-four-hour period and which is called a circadian rhythm (from the Latin for 'about a day'). Bodily and mental alertness are at their lowest during sleep (and especially during slow wave sleep) and tend to peak in the morning and then to start to decline after midday. Body temperature varies with these rhythms, and is highest in the morning and lowest during sleep.

The post-lunch dip

Eating lunch speeds up the decline after midday; lunching reduces energy levels and mental alertness and causes our minds to operate less efficiently. Machine operators are less likely to detect warning signals in the afternoon if they lunch than if they do not. The size of the 'post-lunch dip' in efficiency is similar to that caused by a night without sleep; in some occupations (e.g. air traffic control) this can have serious consequences. To some extent this also depends on personality. Extroverts (who tend to be sociable, spontaneous, and active) are most badly affected, while introverted people, especially those who are fairly emotional, are less affected and may even benefit from lunching. In one study students had an extended period of mental testing between 11 am and 2 pm, but some were allowed to lunch and others not. Most of the non-lunchers performed better than the lunchers at 2 pm, except for two very emotional introverted students who improved after lunch. If you skip lunch your memory and concentration will be better in the afternoon (except if you are particularly emotional and introverted, in which case eating will help your mind work better). In this way our food habits affect our body rhythms.

125

The forty-eight-hour 'day'

Imagine going to live on your own in an underground chamber for weeks on end. All that you need for life is there for you, except contact with other humans. There is no radio or TV and you are so isolated from normal life that you have no clue as to how time is passing. The usual clues, such as changes in dark or light, or in temperature, or in sounds, are absent; you are sealed off. Temperature is constant. You can sleep when you want and eat when you want. What will you do? How will you adjust? What will your eating habits and sleeping habits be?

These are the conditions in which some studies of body rhythms are carried out. Volunteers live for a period in isolation, in caves or underground chambers, where there is no clue at all to the passing of time. Some people carry on their twenty-four-hour circadian rhythm of alertness and sleep just as if they were in the outside world; life goes on as normal. Their body temperature rhythm carries on as normal. Other people continue in the same rhythm but stretch it out over a longer period, often half as long again and sometimes even twice as long. When a 'day' lasts for forty-eight hours it feels to the person just like twenty-four hours. All the intervals within the day are stretched out in proportion to the 'day' length, so that sleep lasts for sixteen hours rather than eight, and so forth. The body temperature cycle changes accordingly. In a forty-eight-hour 'day' lunch occurs half-way through and is the same size as usual (in a twenty-four-hour day). People eat not what they need, but what they are used to. Not surprisingly, people lose weight in these isolation experiments – yet another example of habit dominating food intake; the habit of eating a certain amount of food for lunch overrides any sense of what we need. Living in isolation appears to be an effective, albeit drastic, means of slimming.

Feeding and shift-lag

Body rhythms are also relevant to the eating habits of

shiftworkers. People who work shifts at times when most people are relaxed or asleep (e.g. in the evening or at night) do not adjust their body rhythms. Instead their activities are out of phase with these bodily rhythms; night workers are awake and busy at the very time that their level of alertness and body temperature are at their lowest. They can learn to adapt and compensate, but at a significant cost. Shiftworkers, especially nightworkers, are continuously suffering from shift-lag (just like jet-lag) when they try to take part in the normal life and activities of their family and friends. Instead of reversing all their habits in order to fit in with their shifts they tend to try to keep as closely as possible to their family's usual meal-times and to have their main meal in the evening with the family if this is at all possible – food habits are the last thing to change. Trying to lead a 'normal' life, including eating when your body tells you to sleep, may be one of the things that contribute to the poorer health of shiftworkers. It is very clear that shiftworkers suffer far more than other workers from stomach disorders (such as ulcers), especially from the age of forty onwards. Years of shiftworking add up in their effects. Shiftworkers tend to drink more than others and to take more sleeping tablets. Their dislike of eating food alone and apart from their families illustrates the fact that eating habits have less to do with nutrition than with social and family life.

Feeding rhythms

As well as the twenty-four-hour circadian rhythms there are also shorter cycles throughout the day, similar to the one and a half hour rhythm at night during sleep. These rhythms, of between one and two hours in length (called 'ultradian' rhythms because they are less than a day in length), affect eating. When people are able to eat or drink whenever they want to they do not do so at random; instead there is a peak in eating and drinking every ninety minutes or so (the same length as a sleep cycle). Similar rhythms occur in the activity in the stomach even during sleep. If you were to keep a record of your 'oral' habits – including smoking, if you do smoke – you would be likely to find this wave-like pattern. It is uncanny that this cycle is so clear. Many studies have observed it, and the only variation is in the length of the cycle, from forty minutes to 150 minutes, with an average of ninety. Smokers and ex-smokers have shorter cycles than people who have never smoked; on average their cycles are twenty-five minutes shorter. This means that those who have smoked at some time in their lives experience more peaks of oral activity each day than others, and are perhaps under more pressure to put things in their mouths. If the shorter cycle develops before the smoking habit, then maybe 'short cyclers' are under greater pressure to put things in their mouths. Do binge eaters also show short cycles? We do not know. Later on in this chapter we will come to Freud's idea of the 'oral personality', which claims to explain why some people have more oral habits than others. Perhaps there is a link: as yet no one knows. These findings are very recent and at the edge of our knowledge.

Scientists are only just beginning to describe these basic processes in our behaviour, and are not yet in a position to explain them. Yet recognising that they exist helps us to understand things that might otherwise seem bizarre. One such thing was a case reported by two Scottish sleep experts in the *British Medical Journal* in 1986. This concerned a thirty-seven-year-old male manager who sought psychiatric help because he got up and ate four or five times each night, usually without being clearly awake. In the morning he often failed to remember what had happened. He slept for six nights in a sleep laboratory where his brain activity could be monitored and where his every movement was recorded on videotape. Each night when he went to bed he put near by him packets of biscuits and crisps, a pork pie and two bottles of soft drink. He got up and ate on average five times each night. He awoke briefly to open the biscuit packet or unscrew the bottle top, but once he started eating or drinking he rapidly fell deeply asleep and was in dreaming (REM) sleep within seconds. Eating in his sleep was linked with dreaming sleep and occurred every

100 minutes or so – an example of the ultradian rhythm of oral activity mentioned above. Although this ultradian rhythm usually only causes eating during wakefulness, in this case it broke through during sleep. Understanding such patterns makes this unusual example appear less bizarre.

Short versus long sleepers

Although humans tend to take on average about eight hours sleep each night, some people need more than this and others need less. People vary in their appetite for sleep just as much as they do in their appetite for food, and the two are connected. In general, short sleepers tend to be active, down-to-earth, and full of physical and mental energy, and are often the 'doers' of life. Examples include Margaret Thatcher, Napoleon and Thomas Edison. Long sleepers tend to include more creative writers and philosophers, the 'thinkers' of life. Studies of the eating habits of habitual long and short sleepers find differences between them; long sleepers tend to have more fixed and regular eating habits. In one study researchers classified people's sleeping habits by looking at how much they slept over a period of six months (during which they were satisfied with their sleep). Long sleepers (who averaged more than eight hours' sleep per night) were compared with short sleepers (who averaged less than six hours per night). It was found that long sleepers were much more likely to eat a regular three meals per day while short sleepers tended to deviate from this pattern and snack more, and to report more abnormal eating patterns suggestive of a mild form of eating disorder. Napoleon slept little and ate rapidly – he was reported never to take more than twenty minutes over a meal.

This may be linked to the fact that short sleepers have less dreaming (REM) sleep than long sleepers. There is good evidence from other species that reducing REM sleep disturbs eating habits, and this may also be true of humans. Rats that have been trained to be short sleepers, and thus to cut down their amount of REM sleep, eat much more frequently than other rats, departing from a normal regular feeding pattern as do human short sleepers. We do not yet know whether REM deprivation (caused by short sleep) is or is not the cause of eating habits, but the pattern is intriguing.

What we eat affects how we sleep

What we eat affects how we sleep. Eating to fullness can be soporific, and particular foods can influence sleep quality for good or ill.

Natural foods that bring on sleep

Milky drinks such as Horlicks taken before bedtime have been proved to improve sleep (so that people sleep longer, awaken in the night less often, and move about less while asleep). The benefits are greatest for older adults, aged fifty or more, and tend to be most pronounced in the second half of the night. One reason why milky drinks help is because they contain a naturally occurring substance called tryptophan. This is an interesting substance (an amino acid) because it cannot be manufactured by the human body and so it only enters the body via the food we eat. It enables the body to manufacture another substance, called serotonin, which has profound effects on mood. Serotonin influences our sleep mechanism. Higher serotonin levels cause drowsiness (in the day) and deeper sleep (at night). Therefore the amount of tryptophan we take in as food or drink can affect the serotonin levels in our brain, and thus our moods.

Milky drinks are rich in tryptophan, and are also very easily digested; this may be why they help induce sleep. If adults eat tryptophan-rich food during the daytime they feel drowsy; adding tryptophan to the feeds of bottle-fed new-born infants makes them fall asleep more rapidly and sleep more deeply. It appears to be a natural sedative. Eating a diet free from it increases alertness and impairs sleep. Tryptophan is relatively scarce but can be found in milk, beer, cereal, meat, nuts, bananas, figs and spinach. Carbohydrates are a good source of tryptophan. Eating a meal rich in carbohydrates makes people feel less alert and more fatigued than eating a meal rich in proteins (which generally contain little tryptophan). The exception to this occurs among people who crave carbohydrate foods and binge on them; eating a carbohydrate-rich meal makes them less tired and depressed and more alert! It may be that such binge-eaters crave carbohydrates because of the beneficial effect on their mood. We are beginning to understand the biochemical effects of our diet on the functioning of the brain; further research may give us further insights into the causes of eating disorders.

Normally we take in between 0.5 and 1.5 g tryptophan a day; ingesting more than this produces marked drowsiness. Other things being equal, the more tryptophan you take in the more serotonin is produced, and the drowsier you become.

One of the helpful things about natural sleep-inducing substances like this is that they do not produce hangovers or other side-effects as sleeping tablets do. Sleeping tablets help us to fall asleep more quickly but disturb the nature of sleep so that dreaming sleep is suppressed. When sleeping tablets are discontinued it is just as though a weight is taken off a coiled-up spring, which then rises into the air as it is freed, before eventually settling down to its normal shape. For nights, even weeks, after the tablets are stopped the person experiences a great deal of dreaming sleep (which may be experienced as nightmares). Until the 'rebound effect' is spent and the system has got rid of the effects of the tablets, sleep may well be less satisfying. Tryptophan has no such ill-effects on the nature of sleep.

Natural foods that disturb sleep

Another substance in foods that can affect sleep is caffeine, the active ingredient of tea, coffee, cocoa, and cola drinks. (Coca-Cola originally contained extracts from both the frican caffeine-containing kola nut and the South American coca plant. One of the coca extracts, the powerful stimulant cocaine, was omitted in 1906 and since then the drink has contained other extracts.) The more caffeine you take in the more your sleep is affected (longer to get off, less time asleep etc.); older people are much more affected. The effects of any drug, such as caffeine, very much depend on the individual's personality and how used they are to the drug. Drugs that depress the activity of the brain, such as alcohol, produce their strongest effects on extroverted people, who tend to be sociable, outward going, spontaneous and liking variety. On the other hand drugs such as caffeine, which stimulates the activity of the brain, have their greatest and most rapid effects on introverted people who tend to be reserved, quiet and persistent. Although we tend to regard drinking-chocolate as a calming soporific drink, it does also contain caffeine.

Chocolate came to Europe, like so many other plants, such as maize, potatoes, tomatoes and chillies, after the discovery of the New World by Columbus. The Spanish invading Aztec Mexico in the 1520s came upon cacao for the first time. The Aztecs prized this plant highly and used its beans as currency. They prepared from it a cold foaming liquid to which ground maize rather than milk was added. It was a hot-weather drink, and restricted to males only. They believed that it was divine in origin and that the god Quetzalcoatl had brought it down to earth from paradise. The Aztecs clearly used the drink for its stimulant qualities. One of the invading Spaniards, Bernadino de Sahagun, observed that in moderation: 'It gladdens one, refreshes one, consoles one, invigorates one.' Other Spaniards observed that too much could be intoxicating and addictive, but that even a cup a day could have heartening effects. Like many plants from the New World it was alternately seen as either threatening and sinister or as a mysterious aphrodisiac. Its use as a sexual stimulant was recorded in the French court of Louis xv and even by Casanova.

Losing sleep by losing weight

How much you eat also affects your sleep. During periods of weight loss through dieting people's sleep worsens; during periods of weight gain it improves considerably. The extreme cases of weight loss and gain are seen in, respectively, very obese people on rigorous reducing diets and women emaciated by anorexia nervosa, who are putting on weight as part of their treatment. The same person will sleep far more soundly and for longer when putting on weight than when losing weight. The disturbance to the sleep of normal dieters may not be dramatic but may give rise to unsatisfying sleep and a feeling of tiredness. The reason why weight change affects sleep quality may lie in the purpose of sleep.

We sleep in order to feed the brain

Experts differ as to why we engage in this extraordinary activity called sleep, but our feeding habits appear to be central to the issue. Common sense says that the purpose of sleep is to rest and repair the wear and tear that has happened to the body during the day, but there is virtually no evidence that such 'servicing' or 'repair work' takes place more at night during sleep than at any other time. The only evidence for any sort of repair is in the working of the brain. This is the only organ of the body that goes into a different state during sleep; the changes seen during the sleep cycle are never seen during alertness. Some experts think that during sleep, when the brain is freed from any practical task, it has a chance to benefit from the food that has been taken in during waking hours and engages in a recovery period, when it repairs any wear and tear and also 'digests' experiences of the day. Sleep and feeding are closely connected. We dream so that the brain can benefit from what we have eaten.

Breast-fed children sleep worse than bottle-fed children

The new-born child alternately feeds and sleeps and does little else. Feeding and sleeping rhythms develop together and influence one another. The type of influence depends on the way the child is being fed – by bottle or at the mother's breast. By two months of age there is already a difference; in breast-fed children sleep affects feeding – but not the other way around. The amount of milk the child drinks after a sleep depends on how long it was asleep – but does not affect how long it will sleep after the feed. This is because the child is 'refuelling', and the amount of 'fuel' taken on is affected by the length of the fast while asleep. There is no evidence for the commonsense view that this also works the other way around – that if the child has a bigger feed it will sleep longer afterwards. In bottle-fed children there is little relation between the two; it seems that the breast-fed baby bases its meal size on need but the bottle-fed baby does not. Studies of cats show the same pattern as found in breast-fed babies, but have tied it down even more – demonstrating that how much a cat eats is influenced by the amount of REM (or dreaming) sleep that it has had.

Almost from birth the breast-fed child controls how much milk it drinks at any feed; the breast-fed child has much more control than the bottle-fed child, and tends to consume less. One study of Scottish mothers asked them: 'How do you decide when your child has had enough?' Breastfeeding mothers were seven times more likely than bottle-feeding mothers to stop the meal because the child was falling asleep, and eight times less likely to wait until the child spat out the teat. Breastfeeding allows the baby to let the mother know it has had enough without having to go to the extreme of rejecting the nipple. Having more control allows the breast-fed child to learn to base its meal size on need.

As children grow older their feeding habits affect their sleeping habits even more. Bottle-fed babies begin sleeping through the night much sooner than breast-fed babies, and continue to have less disturbed nights, even at several years of age. In Edinburgh a survey of mothers of two- to four-year-olds found that children who had been breast-fed were still twelve times more likely to awaken in the night than those who had been bottle-fed. The reason for this unfortunate side-effect of breastfeeding is unclear. It is not because of any differences between the two groups of children in how much food they eat, because none was found. Breastfeeding during the first six months of life results in poorer sleep, which is still evident two or three years later. The development of sleeping patterns is affected by early feeding habits.

Do our early eating habits affect our personality?

Can you remember how you were fed as an infant, or how you moved on to solid food? Most people cannot remember anything about this period of their lives, and so it seems paradoxical to suggest that our character has been formed by these events. Yet this is precisely what Sigmund Freud proposed at the beginning of this century and since then the idea has been taken so seriously, that many people assume it to be correct. Freud claimed that experiences we have in infancy determine our personality for the rest of our lives. He suggested that there are several stages in our early life and that how we cope with these will affect our development from then onwards. The first stage is the oral phase; how we negotiate this part of our life, which occurs during the first year, determines how optimistic or pessimistic we are to be as adults. The next stage, the anal phase, is usually met in the third year of life and, according to Freud, affects how obstinate, conscientious, and mean we are to be as adults. Further stages, focusing on the genitals, are supposed to occur at the age of four and at puberty.

Oral personality

Freud's theory about the oral stage emphasises the importance of breastfeeding and weaning, and the habits of sucking and biting. If these events are not dealt with successfully they remain as 'hot' issues affecting the path of further development – in Freud's terms the child is fixated at the oral stage. However, if they are negotiated successfully then they lose all influence on subsequent development. The child who is fixated at the oral stage grows up as an adult who is markedly either optimistic or pessimistic. Which he or she will become depends on how breastfeeding and weaning were dealt with. The infant who is over-indulged with breastfeeding is likely to become an oral optimist, fixated at the sucking stage, with such characteristics as optimism, patience, conviviality, generosity and openness to new ideas. The infant who is frustrated in some way by early feeding practices, for example by being weaned from the mother's breast to solid foods too early, is likely to become an oral pessimist, fixated at the biting stage. The adult oral pessimist is likely to be impatient, hostile, pessimistic, sarcastic (with 'biting' wit), envious and jealous. These descriptions are of extreme cases and, according to Freud's theory, people are likely to vary between these two extremes. Infants who negotiate early feeding successfully grow up without oral fixations and without any of these marked optimistic or pessimistic characteristics.

If Freud's theory were correct it would mean that parents could mould their child's future personality by their feeding practices. Choices such as breastfeeding versus bottle-feeding, and when to introduce solid foods, would become extremely important issues, rather than merely matters of convenience or custom. It would also mean that nations with different early feeding practices should produce citizens with different degrees of optimism or pessimism. Followers of Freud have also argued that wider aspects of human life, such as religious belief, are rooted in oral fixation, because of the similarities between being nurtured, protected and fed as a helpless infant and being cared for by an omnipotent deity. 'God is in his heaven and all's right with the world' is a clear expression of oral optimism. Freud argued that adults who were frustrated at the oral stage (oral pessimists) are particularly prone to depression. Freud's view also predicted that oral personality would affect eating habits, with optimists liking milky, sweet or soft foods that they can suck, and pessimists (with their 'bitter' outlook on life) liking hard or bitter foods that they can bite. Orally fixated people of either kind should also be more likely to develop eating disorders or to display habits to do with their mouths such as smoking or chewing pens. If they give up smoking they need to go on to chew sweets or gum as a substitute, to fulfil their oral needs. They should also be much more likely to take up occupations that involve putting things into their mouths, such as wine tasting, or playing a wind instrument as a professional musician. If the theory were correct it would have far-reaching implications. But is it correct?

Table 7   Oral optimism & pessimism

1	Do you sometimes feel that no matter what you do things will never work out?
2	Keep calm and most things turn out reasonably well?
3	Have you been considered rude because you are not very forthcoming?
4	Are you a good patient when ill?
5	Are you prepared to spend time talking to uninteresting people?
6	Once you are talking, do you often find you can go on and on without difficulty?
7	Do you mind when your friends have more than you do?
8	Is the environment going to be destroyed by pollution in the next fifty years?
9	Are your efforts usually in vain?
10	Do you sometimes know what you want to say but can't say it?
11	Do you, almost without thinking, reject novel ideas?
12	Do you tend to argue with people just for the sake of argument?
13	When you are unwell do you like to be left alone?
14	Do you dislike taking part in fierce debates?
15	Are you one of those people who for some reason are usually bursting with good ideas?
16	Do you really enjoy abusing somebody?
17	It's pointless worrying, for something usually turns up?
18	Do you feel warm to people when you meet them?
19	Do you prefer to work with a group of people to working alone?
20	Are you thought of as patient by those who know you well?

Go to p. 200 to work out your score.
Reprinted with permission from Kline and Storey (1980).

Are you orally fixated?

If you want to find out how orally optimistic or orally pessimistic you are, Table 7 is an opportunity for you to do so. This questionnaire has been produced by Professor Paul Kline at Exeter University in England. If you want to try it, go through the questions fairly quickly, answering each one 'yes' or 'no'. If neither of these answers is exactly right, then choose the one that comes closer to being right.

Freud was over-optimistic

Freud's theory of oral fixation can be tested in several ways. Firstly we can ask whether oral pessimism and oral optimism exist; whether people who are optimistic are also patient, convivial, generous etc., and whether we can measure optimism and pessimism. The answer to these three questions is 'yes'; research finds that, because the characteristics do cluster together we can produce measures such as Kline's, in Table 7.

Secondly, are scores on these measures determined by early feeding history? The problem with this is that most people have no memory of that period of their life, and that mothers have very inaccurate memories of such events. Researchers have visited mothers of young infants regularly through the first few months of life to see their child-rearing practices, and have then gone back to see them a year later. They found that a mother's memory for events such as her child's reaction to weaning was very unreliable. For these reasons it has been hard to tell whether oral fixation is related to early feeding habits.

Thirdly, do cultures with different child-feeding practices produce adults differing in optimism and pessimism? Did the permissive feeding advocated by Dr Spock lead to the permissive society? Some societies wean very late, still breastfeeding four-year-old children; others wean within two months. However, there are no systematic differences in personality between people from these different societies.

Fourthly, do people who differ in oral habits also differ in optimism and pessimism? Paul Kline found that, as predicted, optimists tend to prefer sweet or soft foods like bananas and cream, tapioca, boiled fish and honey, while pessimists prefer hot pickles. Oral pessimists were found to be more likely to smoke or to chew their pens than others.

Conclusion

No one apart from Freud has suggested why cigarette smokers should be more pessimistic than non-smokers, or why optimists should like mushy food. However, until there is clearer evidence we cannot assume that early feeding habits determine personality, though our eating habits do affect, and are affected by, our sleeping habits and our other bodily rhythms. The central importance of our eating habits raises many intriguing questions, including how far eating habits affected the evolution of our species. As we shall see in the next chapter, it has been suggested that human nature was formed by the ways in which our ancestors obtained their food, and that by looking at our nature we see the mark of the past.

8

The mark of the past

Why are there no blue foods? Why are people uneasy about eating alone in public? Why are human beings so co-operative? Why do we prefer sweet foods from birth? Why do men like to carry out tasks in groups? Why do people like restaurants that are dimly lit, and where they can have their backs to the wall? Why does a variety of foods make us eat more? Why do men who never cook in the kitchen like to cook outdoors on barbecues?

We can only start to answer these questions if we take our evolution into account. Human beings have a past, which explains why we are as we are. We have evolved as a species in response to pressures and opportunities that existed; many of those influences were to do with our feeding habits. Our eating habits have been one of the most important influences on our development as a species and have influenced many features of human life, such as our co-operative social nature, tool-making, and differences between the sexes. In this chapter we look at the role of eating in the evolution of Homo sapiens, and try to understand the mark of the past. To do this we need to look at what we know about how our species evolved and at the eating habits of other primates and of the humans who today most resemble our 'natural' selves, hunter-gatherers.

What have we evolved for?

Our species has existed for about 250,000 years; that means that there have been about 10,000 generations of humans, physically identical to us, and all with our mental and emotional capacities. Only during the last 15,000 years have humans lived a settled existence, planting crops and living in fixed places; only in the last 10,000 years have cities existed (Jericho being the oldest). The rate of change in human life has accelerated during the last 1,000 years, and especially in the last 500, with the development of printing, mechanised transport, science, modern medicine, and so on. The population has increased faster and faster, so that the majority of all humans who *have ever lived* are alive today. Since the development of agriculture 600 generations have passed, and since the development of printing twenty generations have existed. So 'civilisation' has existed for only the last four per cent of human generations, a period that is so short in evolutionary terms that no real change has occurred in it. So, in the sense that we as a species have evolved to live in a certain way of life, civilised life is not 'natural' for us. What, then, is our 'natural' way of life?

Our natural way of life?

The natural way of life, to which we are biologically fitted, is one in which food is acquired from naturally available supplies, by hunting and killing animals and by gathering fruit, vegetables and nuts. This hunter-gatherer's way of life, which ninety-four per cent of human generations have lived, has become less and less common over the last ten centuries; today it is carried on by only a few societies, such as Eskimos in the Arctic, bushmen in the Kalahari desert of Namibia and the Aborigines of Australia. Today the hunter-gatherer's way of life is under increasing threat; many of these populations have either been pushed out to more and more arid or unproductive land, or changed by contact with other societies (e.g. the Eskimos now have motorised sledges). We can learn a lot about the life man used to lead by looking at remaining hunter-gatherer societies, before they vanish for ever. This knowledge can also help us to reconstruct our evolutionary history.

Although if any way of life is 'natural' for us it is the hunter-gatherer's lifestyle, most humans no longer live it. Many of the characteristics that helped us to be successful in that lifestyle are inappropriate and unhelpful in the lives we lead today. For example, the natural stress response of increased mental and physical arousal upon encountering threat was of great value when most threats were physical and could be dealt with by physical action. When the body is aroused by threat it undergoes physiological changes that prepare it for vigorous activity; the heart pumps blood faster, the liver releases starch which is converted into blood sugar, breathing becomes deeper, chemicals are released to enable the blood to clot more quickly: these and other changes enable the person under threat to act rapidly and vigorously. This response to threat, of preparing the body for 'fight or flight', was valuable to hunter-gatherers when threats were of a kind that could be dealt with in that way. It is much less appropriate as a response to the kind of threats met in modern Western society, for example overload in the work of a manager. Such problems require an entirely different response and, under sustained stress, the body's hunter-gatherer response may cause illnesses such as gastric ulcers or hypertension, or even 'get stuck' and tip the sufferer into a state of generalised anxiety.

What is adaptive, in evolutionary terms, depends upon the circumstances in which a species lives. What was valuable in the far past may be harmful today. For example, the preference for sweet-tasting foods was exceptionally valuable in guiding humans to eat energy-rich foods when most easily available foods were not high in energy. Today this preference is exceptionally harmful, because modern technology has produced so many energy-rich refined foods, and the need is to reduce consumption of energy: a 'sweet tooth' is a liability rather than a help. In the same way the effects of variety in boosting food intake may have proved helpful in influencing hunter-gatherers to eat a wide variety of foods (and thus take in needed nutrients), but are harmful today through influencing overconsumption of energy-rich, nutrient-free foods made available through food technology.

Hunter-gatherer societies that we know about exist in a range of environments including the arid deserts of Australia, the Arctic (where there is little vegetation to gather, but many large mammals to hunt), and the food-rich forests of Zaire, inhabited by the pygmies. Experts on human evolution believe that the ancestors of Homo sapiens first evolved on the great plains of Africa, emerging from forests into the savannah at a time of great changes in climate and vegetation some seven million years ago. That is the environment out of which we have evolved; that is our natural home.

What have we evolved from?

Our species, Homo sapiens, is a member of the primates and originally evolved, like all of them, from a common ancestor. This was a small nocturnal insect-eating creature which no longer exists today, but which may have been like the bush baby. The different types of monkeys and apes that exist today have many ancestors in common, but have gradually grown apart over time. The groups from which we last diverged (and to which we are most similar) are the chimpanzees. It is important to note that humans (and our ancestors, the hominids) never were bush babies, baboons, gorillas, or chimpanzees. We and all these other primate species which exist today have evolved from different ancestors which now no longer exist.

Archaeologists are trying to establish some of the earlier types of hominids from fragments of their bones, which have been discovered all over the world, but particularly in East Africa. In recent years our relationships with existing primates have been studied by looking at our biochemical similarities with them; the more similar we are, the more recently we diverged from a common stock. This study has indicated much closer relationships than had previously been supposed, and implies that Homo sapiens emerged much more recently than had been thought. Biochemical studies have found that we, as a species, are so similar to chimpanzees as to have ninety-eight per cent of our DNA in common; this makes the two of us more alike than are rats and mice.

Our common ancestor with the apes (*proconsul*) was a small creature, the size of a baboon, which lived in trees and ate mainly fruit. Proconsul lived in the extensive forests that covered Africa some twenty-two million years ago. About fifteen million years ago the ancestor of the present-day orang utan diverged from our ancestors, followed by the ancestor of the gorilla at about ten million years ago. Our ancestor, *ramapithecus,* from whom these lines diverged continued to live in the forests until its world was dramatically altered by the changes in the climate of Africa that occurred some seven or eight million years ago. The forests shrank and were largely replaced by the great African plains and savannahs that we see today. Our ancestors diverged from the forest-dwelling ancestors of chimpanzees to take advantage of the opportunities of this new environment and the first hominids (man-like primates) called *australopithecus* (Latin for 'southern ape') emerged. These walked upright on two feet. Australopithecus lived on the East African savannah about four million years ago and was the direct ancestor of a succession of our ancestors who became more and more like us. The most modern form of our species emerged 40,000 years ago, but Homo sapiens has been in existence for a quarter of a million years. There is evidence that stone tools were used two million years ago, and fire one million years ago. Until the development of agriculture 15,000 years ago Homo sapiens had lived a hunter-gatherer's existence.

Our ancestors' eating habits

Where did our eating habits fit into our ancestral history? Our ancestors were successful because they were able to adapt to the new open country and thrive on the opportunities presented there. In the forest in which ramapithecus had lived, the main sources of food were fruit, leaves and insects. Australopithecus evolved to take advantage of a wider range of food available, including game, which they hunted in an organised manner. The development of hunting in this way influenced our development into hunter-gatherers like those we see today. That change to a hunting way of life was crucial, and responsible for the development of many unique human features. It probably amplified and extended several features of hominid social life – including co-operation, kin networks and the division of labour between the sexes – and hastened the development of early technology such as the harnessing of fire and the use of food storage and hunting implements. Hunting large game requires the co-operation of many adult males, and will only be successful if there is some means of ensuring that all members of the group – rather than the individual who kills the beast – enjoy a share of the flesh. As we shall see below, primitive hunting and food-sharing can be seen in species such as the chimpanzee, while much more complex social rules governing the sharing of food occur in most hunter-gatherer societies.

Becoming hunters

Although hunting might be seen as aggressive because it involves slaughtering animals, it does in fact stimulate many non-aggressive features, such as sharing between humans (and, presumably, human ancestors such as australopithecus).

146

Another feature of hunting in both humans and chimpanzees is that it is an activity carried out solely by adult males; females and young do not take part. This is because hunting often involves following creatures for long distances, an activity which is difficult for children or females who are pregnant or lactating – as adult females generally were. Females would also be a liability because of odours associated with menstruation or lactation, which are easily detected by potential prey or predators. Even today women (especially menstruating women) are attacked by predators much more often than men are. For these and other reasons males hunted while females continued to gather vegetation for food – and this can be seen in chimpanzees and hunter-gatherers today. Dependence on hunting gave rise to such uniquely human traits as transporting killed food to a home site for sharing with other members of the group, and led to the development of containers for food, and equipment to prepare the food. The development of more complex systems of killing animals larger than men led to the invention of tools such as hunting implements, and even language. Thus the new opportunities for acquiring food produced pressures that caused human nature to develop as it has. In order to appreciate this more fully we shall look at the feeding habits of our primate relatives, and of contemporary hunter-gatherer societies.

The eating habits of today's primates

Most primates that exist today are omnivores. Despite living in different settings most eat fruit (ninety per cent of species), insects (sixty-five per cent), and mature leaves and the soft parts of plants such as buds, shoots, and flowers (seventy per cent). About thirty per cent eat the flesh or eggs of species other than insects. Only the primitive nocturnal tree shrews (which are similar to the ancestor of all primates) are specialists and eat just one food – insects. Although some primates eat a great deal of one of these types of food (and are therefore called

147

folivores, leaf-eaters, or frugivores, fruit eaters), most primates are omnivorous, and few are purely vegetarian. Chimpanzees, the primates closest to us, eat everything. They live in woodlands and their habits may be very similar to those that our australopithecine ancestors took out into the Great African Plains. Our ancestors probably had chimpanzee eating habits before they became hunters.

Chimpanzee feeding habits

Chimpanzees eat everything from leaves to caterpillars, and from honey to lichens. They eat at least as wide a range of substances as human hunter-gatherers living near them. They also show some habits which have previously been thought to be uniquely human – the use of tools, co-operative hunting, and food-sharing. Feeding takes up half of their waking hours, and most of their feeding time is concerned with vegetation.

Only adult male chimpanzees hunt, and they do this in groups of up to nine or ten at a time, preying on creatures of their own size or smaller, such as other small monkeys or antelopes. Each adult chimpanzee eats about 10 kg (23 lb) of meat per year. They rarely scavenge or eat dead creatures, eating only what they themselves kill. Chimpanzees stalk their prey in absolute silence, often positioning themselves around the prey so as to cut off its escape routes. Then they rush at their prey and kill it rapidly, frequently whooping and screaming as they do so. The whole group of chimpanzees at the kill share the flesh between themselves and eat it on the spot; this is often a period of intense social interaction, lasting for several hours. Of all the time involved in hunting, from stalking to eating, ninety per cent is spent on sharing food. This, together with the fact that hunting usually occurs after feeding on fruit, demonstrates that its motivation is social rather than nutritional. No chimpanzee has ever been observed to kill and eat privately. Food-sharing maintains and deepens social bonds.

By contrast, collecting and eating insects is a predominantly female activity, although males may often snack on insects and fruit. Chimpanzees often employ implements to help them get at insects; the most common tools are sticks used to prise termites from termite hills.

Our ancestors' feeding habits

On leaving the forests to exploit the savannah, our ancestors took with them chimpanzee feeding habits, but these were adapted and transformed by the demands of the new environment. Hunting left its mark on our species. Its most important effect was to promote our co-operative nature. Altruistic behaviour gave the hominids an advantage over other, more selfish, species. Food-sharing provided a more constant supply of food, and thus resulted in better-fed individuals who were more successful in breeding. Other effects were to encourage our ancestors to adopt an upright posture (so as to give rapid chase), and to accentuate psychological differences between the sexes to allow a more efficient division of labour. Hunting fostered the 'male bond', the preference of men to spend time together in groups, for work or leisure. There was also pressure to develop language and abstract thought, so as to make it possible to discuss future events and make plans. There was a definite advantage in specialising and developing one particular part of the body, the brain. Intelligence, language and thought all developed as part of our ancestors' exploitation of the food opportunities offered by their new environment. Our ancestors' feeding habits made us what we are today. This can be seen most clearly when we look at people today who still live the life of the hunter-gatherer.

The feeding habits of hunter-gatherers

Hunter-gatherers lead a leisurely life, with relatively little time spent at 'work', and much time spent in 'play' – social, ceremonial, or other pursuits. Such societies still flourish today where they have not been disturbed by contact with agricultural or industrial societies. Most – such as the bushmen of the Kalahari – live on land that nobody else wants. They thrive because they are so well adapted to life there. They tend to base their diet on the most reliable type of food available, which is usually gathered vegetables, but often shellfish or fish. To this basic foodstuff is added meat from hunting. Gathering, usually carried out by women, contributes most to the diet but is least valued by the society. Hunting, a male activity, is a much less reliable way of obtaining food and contributes least to the diet. Hunting is a glamorous male activity which brings in very little in comparison to the female activity of gathering. Most hunter-gatherers 'eat as much vegetable foodstuff as they need and as much meat as they can' (in the words of a leading researcher into the bushmen). The exception is the Eskimos, who have few plants to gather, and so base at least ninety per cent of their diet on fishing and hunting. Hunter-gatherer tribal rituals and story-telling celebrate the value of hunting, but rarely that of gathering vegetation.

Why is hunting and meat-eating celebrated and valued so highly by these societies? Meat certainly has great nutritional value; it is a rich source of energy and protein, but it is not the only one, neither is it vital to the diet. For example, the Kalahari bushmen base their diet on the mongongo nut, which is constantly available and in sufficient quantities to supply most of their nutritional needs. Eating 300 nuts (weighing together 175 g (7 oz) and easily collected in four hours) provides 1,300 calories and 56 g (2 oz) of protein, which is equivalent to that supplied by 500 g (1 lb 2 oz) of beef. Vegetation, insects (which are often present within vegetation), and earth (which is often eaten) can usually supply adequate nutrition. The social functions of hunting and meat-eating, already present in chimpanzees, are elaborated and intensified in most hunter-gatherer groups and may account for the prestige status of meat. The consumption of meat brings more leisure time and provides opportunities for more socialising. Hunting big game (an activity never seen in any other primates) requires and fosters co-operation, and results in extensive food-sharing and feasting among the group.

The advantages of sharing food

There are great advantages for a group of hunters in co-operating closely and sharing the results of any individual kill widely. In this way they have a wide range of options. They can stalk large prey together as a group, or they can co-ordinate their efforts and disperse individually or in pairs and cover a very wide area systematically. The more hunters involved in the search for prey, the more likely it will be found by one of them on any particular day, and the more predictable a source of food it becomes for the group as a whole. Bushmen hunters are only successful on average on one day in four, and so if between four and eight families hunt in a co-ordinated way and pool their meat, meat will be available to the group on most days. Some types of Eskimos go out hunting alone in winter when their prey is very scarce; by dividing up the search area and sharing the results hunting becomes much more efficient. Hunting is a prestige activity because it fosters co-operation in many ways and its evolution was critical in the evolution of human nature.

Hunter-gatherers tend to live in groups of between twenty-five and fifty, mainly composed of kin, but are often in close contact with other groups and join together with them in large camps (bushmen) or for ceremonial feasts (Aborigines) during seasons when game is most available. The availability of food determines the social and cultural life beyond the family group or clan. Who shares food with you marks which group you are in; it is the most important expression of belonging. In most such societies there is a very strict code of conduct about sharing, which prevents the person who made the kill from taking 'the lion's share'. For example, among the pygmies of Zaire game that is killed is taken back to camp by the hunters. The food is distributed by the hunters who wounded or killed the beast, their kin having priority, but all members of the band receiving some. Internal organs, such as the heart and liver, are highly valued and go to the elders of the band; the intestines go to women and children, and the head goes to men. The hunter who killed the beast sits silently at the public fire, modestly feigning indifference, while the other hunters recount the story of the hunt. This social custom ensures that the flesh is shared throughout the band.

In a similar way Australian Aborigines traditionally valued hunting, even though until very recently eighty per cent of the food eaten was gathered vegetation, collected in two or three hours each day. Hunting was much more unreliable, but a constant preoccupation of men, who tended to go out with groups of three or four relatives in search of large game such as wallabies and emus. Animals that were killed were shared between the hunters and taken back to camp (usually composed of ten to thirty individuals) for further subdivision. The man who killed the beast took his share last of all, even if only the entrails were left. Certain relatives of his had particularly strong claims, for example his father-in-law had the highest priority. The catch was rapidly shared between members of the band, roasted, and eaten almost immediately (Aborigines never boiled food). This arrangement of food-distribution meant that any hunter and his relatives would receive food whenever a kill was made.

In hunter-gatherers we can see most clearly the support for the idea that sharing food was a very important influence on our evolution. If our ancestors had never had to hunt for food on the savannah, our species would not have developed in its present form, or anything like it. Human nature was moulded by our food habits.

What is the 'mark of the past'?

Where else can we see our hunting heritage? The hunter-gatherer's way of life may be natural for us, but in the modern world we do not follow it. Pushing a trolley around a supermarket is like gathering (and is predominantly a female activity) but it is hard to find a similarity to hunting (beyond jobs like selling insurance, which involve groups of males hunting for custom in a co-ordinated way). However, there may be marks of the past if we have eyes to see them. We have already looked at the ways our omnivore heritage produces the variety effect, taste aversions, and the liking for sweetness. But why should humans not like blue foods? There are virtually no popular blue foods; imagine how distasteful it would be to eat blue baked beans, blue meat, or to drink blue fruit squash. One reason for this may lie in the primitive association of blue with toxic mould.

Why do we feel uncomfortable about eating alone in public, and prefer to eat in privacy? Why are the most expensive restaurants dimly lit, with tables far apart, low noise level, and – often – a real fire? What is the reason for the popularity of flambé dishes in restaurants? And why are men who never cook indoors drawn to cook meat on camp fires or on barbecues? It has been suggested that each of these phenomena betrays our origins. Our hominid ancestors were vulnerable to predation by carnivores, and were most at risk at the moment of eating. When eating you are static and cannot flee easily, and the smell of the dead flesh, whether raw or cooked, attracts predators to you. Unlike some of our primate cousins (such as gorillas), our hominid ancestors could easily be taken by predators; their only defence was in their intelligence. Leaving the forest meant leaving the safety of sleeping in nests in trees (like chimpanzees); places like caves gave some safety, and fire added to that. Therefore cave-like surroundings, with a feeling of privacy (e.g. one's back against the wall or in a corner) and flames offer the surroundings most guaranteed to still our primitive anxieties or ambivalence about eating in public. In such a setting meat, especially rare or bloody meat, seems natural. These are the surroundings and food offered by the most exclusive restaurants, which make diners feel comfortable and persuade them to linger. By contrast fast-food restaurants, which encourage diners to refuel and leave as rapidly as possible, provide the opposite milieu – bright lights, seats close together, often with diners' backs facing the gangway, a high level of sound, and the food camouflaged in polystyrene containers and other forms of opaque packaging. Such restaurants make diners, especially lone ones, particularly uncomfortable and encourage people to eat and leave. This is because they play on our primitive fears.

Humans who eat in public places behave similarly to gazelles and other species who are vulnerable to predators. In both cases individuals frequently throw glances around, scanning their surroundings. The frequency of scanning depends on the group size; the smaller the group, the more any individual scans. In gazelles on the savannah this is highly adaptive, because it means that one creature is always on watch, and if it sees a potential predator it can alert its fellow feeders. The same is true of humans; detailed studies of people eating in cafés, restaurants and other public places show that the smaller the group the more time is spent in scanning. Individuals eat most rapidly and leave soonest; eating alone in public is not a relaxing experience. Could this be a mark of the past?

Men like to spend their leisure time together in groups, whether these are clubs, sports teams, groups of pub regulars, or committees; bonds between groups of men arise more naturally than among groups of women. Is this a hangover from the co-operative hunting group? Men who never normally cook enjoy cooking meat over a camp fire or barbecue. Men (not women) ritually 'kill' (carve) joints of meat and distribute it among their kin and companions. Can these be residual pleasures from the satisfaction of sharing, cooking, and eating meat after the hunt?

These speculations cannot be proved or disproved in the same way as most in this book, by carrying out experiments, because they are speculations about the past. Looking at our present habits and asking why they should be the way they are encourages us to look at them in a fresh way. If the above speculations are incorrect, then why do these 'hunting' themes keep intruding into our eating habits? It is not enough to dismiss these speculations as far-fetched; the phenomena they seek to explain are so familiar to us as to be invisible, yet they may be the points in our lives that show the mark of the past.

Conclusion

Our far-distant ancestors had to adapt to changing circumstances and adopt a hunter-gatherer's way of life. The new ways of acquiring food affected the ways in which human nature evolved, particularly in the direction of co-operation and sociability.

9

What has eating got to do with obesity?

Eating habits have very little to do with the cause of obesity, but a great deal to do with its treatment.

The survival of the fattest

Most human beings have regarded obesity as beautiful and desirable. Concern about weight is so widespread today that it is easy to forget how recent and how localised this is. Obesity has been prized and seen as attractive for most of recorded history and in most human societies this century. Thinness has been seen as unattractive and has been feared because of its association with illness. One of the earliest works of art that survive today, the Venus of Willendorf – a 25,000 year old piece of sculpture found in Austria – celebrates the beauty of the ample female form. The Venus was produced during the Neolithic Age, when there was a transition from hunting and gathering to a more settled existence based on agriculture. From then until 200 years ago in Europe (and, of course, still today in many parts of the world) the availability of food was often unpredictable, suffering annual variations and occasional catastrophic shortages. There were famines in

England as late as the eighteenth century; up until then the average life expectancy was about thirty years. Only those at the head of society were protected from these fluctuations in food supply; starvation was a real possibility for those at the bottom. Living constantly with the threat of starvation resulted in widespread malnutrition and low resistance to infectious diseases, from which many died. It was the survival of the fattest. Fatness was associated with health and access to the good things in life, and often valued as attractive or as a symbol of status. This is reflected in the work of artists such as Rubens, who celebrated the beauty of fatness. Henry VIII was admired when, in his fifties, his waist increased to fifty-four inches; Edward VII who, at his coronation, had both chest and waist measurements of forty-eight inches had been affectionately dubbed 'Prince Tum-tum'. In the Victorian age the desire not to be thin was even the subject of diet books explaining how to put on weight, such as T. C. Duncan's *How to become plump*, published in 1878.

The effects of poor diet were shown in the First World War when conscripts were examined. Of every nine men called up only three were in good health; two were fairly unfit, three very unfit, and one a chronic invalid. Much of this poor health was due to chronic malnutrition. There was little improvement after the war; this was one of the reasons for the introduction of a milk subsidy in the depressed 1920s. In 1931 a national advisory committee on food was set up to look at how the national diet could be improved; its concern was how to increase the amount of milk and meat consumed. (Ironically a similar national advisory committee set up fifty years later – NACNE – concerned itself with the importance of reducing the amount of milk and meat in the diet, so as to prevent coronary heart disease.) In the 1920s and 1930s infectious diseases such as TB killed many people and malnutrition increased vulnerability to them. A fatter baby was truly a 'bonny baby' when the norm was to have a thin baby (and this attitude has continued inappropriately today).

Fatness as the conspicuous result of consumption

Only within the last few decades in the West have thin women been seen as attractive and desirable. The Duchess of Windsor claimed that: 'For a woman it is impossible to be too thin or too rich.' Though the Duchess was clearly wrong – being underweight is as unhealthy in many ways as being over-weight – a streamlined shape continues to be fashionable and had been shown even in the dimensions of women who appear in *Playboy* centrefolds and become Miss America. From 1959 to 1979 *Playboy* models and beauty queens became pro-gressively thinner; each year the average weight of Miss America dropped by nearly half a pound. In contrast, over the same period the weight of the average American woman of the same age increased by nearly half a pound a year, so that the discrepancy between reality and the image of beauty doubled each year. There was also a steady increase in the numbers of magazine articles about slimming over the two decades. Slimness has been an increasingly important concern and standard of female beauty. Recent surveys in the USA and Britain show that fewer than one woman in twenty-five considers herself to be too thin and that at any time sixty per cent of women are dieting. This trend is much more marked for women than men because judgements about women's attractiveness are much more strongly based on physical characteristics.

Outside of modern industrial societies fatness is still pre-ferred. In some societies fat women are still seen as the most attractive and women are fattened up for marriage. A century ago in Uganda Speke and other British explorers reported that prior to marriage some young women were confined to 'fattening huts', where they were fed a diet of milk. Eventually they became so fat that they could not walk. Speke likened them to beached seals. Where food is scarce fatness is the conspicuous result of consumption, representing a form of food hoarding that only the rich can afford. The preference for fat women is still very much a minority taste in the West, and is catered for in the USA by clubs for Fat Admirers, men who are sexually attracted by only very obese women, the more obese the better. In that subculture as elsewhere, women's worth is still based on their weight – the only difference is in whether more or less weight is preferred. In Western societies today the higher social classes are thinner than the lower; this pattern is reversed in Third World countries such as India and Egypt.

The slimming industry

The people who worry about obesity today are the female inhabitants of the industrialised Western countries who spend large amounts of money each year on slimming products. One in four of all American women have enrolled in a weight-reduction programme (e.g. Weight Watchers) at least once; one in ten women who have never in their lives been overweight have enrolled in such a programme! Diet books are best-sellers; *The F-Plan Diet* sold more copies than any other book in its year of publication. The intensity and moral tone of some dieting organisations resemble those of a religion.

Prejudice against obese people

The widespread concern to be slim coincides with evidence that becoming slimmer would increase the health of obese people. In this way it differs from other pressures to conform to views of attractiveness that are essentially unhealthy and crippling – such as footbinding in China, which aimed to produce another characteristic of the aristocracy, small feet. However, the pressure to be slim also extends to people of normal weight whose health would not benefit from their losing weight. The popular concern about body weight harms two groups of people – those for whom it becomes an overwhelming concern and who develop eating disorders (see Chapter 10) and those who are discriminated against because they are obese. As we shall see below, obese people do little, if anything, to cause themselves to become overweight, and the

160

prospect for them to become lastingly slim is unpromising. Yet instead of being sympathetic towards people suffering from this unattractive and hazardous burden, most people are critical and unsympathetic, blame obese people for being obese, and act in a negative way towards them. As Judy Mazel wrote (in her best-seller, *The Beverley Hills Diet*): 'Being fat is an obscenity – we are shunned, scorned, and ridiculed. A failure for all to see – and mock.'

The stereotype of the obese person is of a weak, unhappy person who lacks the self-control that others are presumed to possess and who has 'let herself go'. This is the view given by, for example, people who watch a video of a brief interview with someone and then describe their impressions of that person. If the same person behaved identically in two interviews, but in one appears to be of normal weight and in the other as very overweight, the viewing audience consistently rates the 'overweight' person much more negatively. Just knowing someone's weight strongly affects the impressions that people form of that person. This stereotyping of prejudice (pre-judging the person) is pervasive and affects those who should know better, including members of the medical profession and indeed obese persons themselves. These views affect people's actions towards obese people. Studies have shown that obese people are less likely to be successful than 'normal' people in obtaining either lodgings or a college place. Discrimination against obese people takes forms that would be illegal if directed towards blacks or women, and this 'weightist' view is even expressed by official organisations who attempt to force their members to lose weight. As an example consider the policy of the US Army where a regulation (600–9) states that 'excessive body fat . . . connotes a lack of personal discipline', and states the need to 'present a trim military appearance at all times'. The three-quarters of a million men and women in the US Army are subject to assessments of their degree of fatness. If their weight exceeds a maximum allowable weight (based on their height, age and sex) and there is no medical cause for this, they are obliged to take part in a weight-control programme. Failure to make satisfactory progress in this can lead to discharge, with loss of retirement benefit. Men and women are obliged to take part in this process whether or not they are functioning adequately in their post.

The stigma associated with obesity is often taken to heart by obese people, who harbour very negative views of themselves and of other obese people. One response to this stigma has been the development of pressure groups to counter discrimination; in the USA the National Association of Fat Americans and the Fat Liberation Front have been very active in bringing test cases to the courts and disseminating accurate information about obesity.

The causes of obesity

There is no one cause of obesity. The commonsense assumption that fat people are fat because they eat more than other people is certainly wrong. Surveys show that, in general, obese people do not eat more than non-obese people. Knowing what someone eats cannot help you to predict their weight.

Social factors

Several factors are involved in causing and maintaining obesity, and any explanation must be able to account for these. Social class is one of the most important factors, especially for women; in the West members of different classes do not differ much in weight, but those from higher social classes tend to be taller and less often obese. People who climb the social ladder tend to become thinner; those who drop down to a lower social class than the one they were born in tend to become heavier.

Genetic factors

Fatness tends to run in families; fat parents tend to have fat children and thin parents thin children. This influence is probably partly due to the inheritance of fatness-producing genes, but that is not the whole story. Obese people also tend to have obese spouses, and the fatness of a person's parent is a good predictor of the fatness of their spouse! The adopted children of obese persons (who are not genetically similar to them) are fatter than those of non-obese persons. Even the dogs of obese persons are fatter than the dogs of non-obese persons! It is likely that the fatness of a pet dog can be predicted by the fatness of its owner's parents. Clearly none of these relationships can be explained by genetics, and so this is not the only explanation of why fatness tends to run in families. Families share food, activities, social environment, income, etc., and many of these factors may affect weight. It is clear that the family atmosphere affects how successful weight reduction will be in the long term; women who have lost weight are much more likely to regain it if their husbands are generally critical towards them.

Energy imbalance

Obesity develops through an energy imbalance in which more energy is taken in than expended. Energy intake comes from food. If intake and expenditure balance one another, then the amount of fat in the body remains constant. If intake exceeds expenditure, then energy is stored in the body as fat (500 g/1 lb for each 3,500 calories); if it is less, the body draws on its fat reserves and there is a loss of weight. Fat is a way of storing energy; 500 g (1 lb) would run a 100-watt light bulb for forty hours. Most of energy expenditure is accounted for by metabolic needs – the energy used by the body to keep going, and which would be needed even for lying in bed all day. The amount of energy taken up by physical activity is relatively small in comparison, except in the case of unusually vigorous exercise such as a ten-mile run. Metabolic rates are more or less constant for any one person but vary with age and body weight. Heavier and younger people have higher metabolic rates; losing weight reduces the metabolic rate. In addition there are very wide ranges of difference between individuals. In 1961 two researchers assembled pairs of individuals, of the same weight, age and sex, and with the same activity level as each other, but who ate vastly different amounts of food. In some pairs one person regularly ate twice as much as the other, although both maintained the same steady weight.

Brown fat

It follows that some people are much more vulnerable to obesity because they have low energy needs. The cause of such low needs is still unclear; one suggestion currently under investigation is that people with high energy needs waste much more energy by radiating it off as heat, like an electric fire with three bars on rather than just one. The crucial difference between people with high and low needs is thought to lie in the amount of brown fat in their body. This is a distinctive type of fatty tissue found in deposits within the body, the actual amount varying markedly from one person to the next. It is supposed to control how much energy is wasted in this way. This theory is still being investigated. As yet no clearly acceptable explanation of the cause of obesity has yet been put forward. It is unlikely that one single factor will be identified as 'the cause' of obesity; there are probably a range of different ways of becoming and staying obese. In Shakespeare's words from *Twelfth Night*: 'Some are born great, some achieve greatness, and some have greatness thrust upon them.'

Why care about obesity?

Most people who are concerned about their weight are motivated by the attractiveness of their appearance in a society which sees thin as beautiful. Is slimming then merely a matter of vanity? Many people worry about obesity; should they?

Obesity and health

Obesity carries real risks to health, especially in extreme cases, but there is no close relationship between these risks and the concern about weight. The greatest risk (in terms of dropping dead suddenly or dying prematurely) is for the very over-weight rather than the mildly overweight, for males rather than females, and for the young rather than for the old. There is a great contrast between the people who are at risk from fatness and those who show most enthusiasm for dieting, who are mildly overweight females. The two groups who suffer most from society's attitude to obesity are young obese men (who have most to benefit from slimming, but receive little encouragement) and mildly overweight women (who have little benefit from slimming, but are under great pressure to do it).

Greater weight is associated with reduced life expectancy. As Shakespeare made Henry say to Falstaff: 'Know the grave doth gape for thee thrice wider than for other men.' Obesity also carries a greater risk of developing high blood pressure, diabetes, gall-bladder disease and cancer, and greater risks of complications during pregnancy and during surgery. Obese people are three times more likely to suffer from either hypertension or diabetes, and very obese women are five times more likely to suffer endometrial cancer. Where the fat is deposited in the body makes a difference to its dangerousness; fat deposits within the abdomen (the 'pot belly') are under the heart and therefore more dangerous than the same amount deposited elsewhere, for example in the buttocks. It is safer to be pear-shaped than apple-shaped.

The benefits of weight loss

Losing weight can reduce many of these risks, for example it can bring high blood pressure down to normal as effectively as antihypertensive medication; reducing to a lower weight can make someone live longer. Reducing weight can help some people to live happier and longer lives, and the people to benefit most are those most at risk – young very obese males. The fact that most slimmers are mildly overweight females shows that slimming has little to do with health, and much more to do with current conceptions of beauty.

Are obese people different?

Obese people differ from others in having more fat in their bodies. Do they differ psychologically in any way? It has been suggested that they differ in personality, in their eating habits, and in what turns on their appetite.

Are obese people different in personality?

Many people believe that obese people differ from others and this prejudice is reflected in discrimination against the obese. The notion that body weight is linked to personality is not new. Shakespeare has Julius Caesar remark: 'Let me have men about me that are fat. . . . Yond Cassius has a lean and hungry look; he thinks too much: such men are dangerous.' The implication is that thin people are more ambitious, motivated and discontented. At some time or another, almost every possible suggestion about the personality of obese people has been made – that they are either more anxious than others, or less anxious, weaker or stronger, or different in some other way. One very influential view has been put forward by psychoanalysts, such as Hilda Bruch. This is that becoming obese is a way of coming to terms with deep psychological problems, of which the person may not even be conscious. As a result the obese person is free from anxiety or emotional upset. Bruch argued that weight reduction would deprive obese people of this resolution and precipitate psychological or emotional problems.

Does this happen? The most relevant evidence comes from looking at very obese people who lose dramatically large amounts of weight, for example people who undergo intestinal bypass surgery. In this type of operation the middle section of the intestines is bypassed: the upper section is reconnected to the lower section, thereby 'leapfrogging' the intervening middle section. Only part of the intestine is still functioning, so only part of the food eaten will be absorbed; the person can carry on eating normally while the intestine 'diets'. In the months after bypass surgery people lose very large amounts of weight, often halving their body weight, without making any effort. If psychoanalysts like Bruch were correct then we would expect to see a big increase in emotional distress in these people; the dramatic changes in their weight should deprive them of their means of coping with their unconscious problems. In fact we see the opposite; people become less distressed and upset, and more self-confident. The same pattern is seen after people lose smaller amounts of weight using other, non-surgical, means. This shows that Bruch's view is clearly incorrect: obesity is not a response to unconscious psychological conflicts or problems.

The reason why some psychoanalysts have suggested that there is something amiss psychologically with obese people is that they only see people who have something amiss: psychologically healthy obese people (like psychologically healthy non-obese people) do not consult them. The only way of seeing whether there are any differences between obese and non-obese persons is to look at random samples of the population at large. Surveys in which this has been done have consistently failed to find any clear personality or psychological differences between the obese and the non-obese; therefore knowing a person's weight does not reveal anything about personality, and theories which imply that it does are incorrect.

Do obese people have different eating habits?

Many people have suggested that obese people eat differently. The 'obese eating style' is said to involve eating rapidly, chewing food little, and eating everything on the plate. This style was thought to contribute to obesity because it results in a large quantity of food being eaten quickly, before the development of any satiety, which might otherwise reduce the amount eaten. It was thought that people who had other appetite-related problems were similar – e.g. alcoholics were thought to drink more rapidly and in bigger gulps. Because of the implications for treatment (if obese persons could learn to eat like the non-obese they would be able to diet more easily) the 'obese eating style' was searched for high and low. About fifty studies have been reported, mainly involving watching people eat in public places such as restaurants and cafés, but also in laboratories and in their own homes. Rather like birdwatchers, researchers sat unobtrusively, stop-watch in hand, watching diners from the moment they selected their food to the moment they left the table, counting the numbers of mouthfuls, the chewing rate, the pauses between mouthfuls, and so on. In some studies the researchers even weighed the leftovers on plates after the diner had left. The results were clear-cut. There are no consistent differences between the eating styles of obese and non-obese people; the obese eating style simply does not exist. Just as knowing a woman's weight tells us nothing about her personality, so it tells us nothing about her eating style. One of the interesting findings from this research was how much the same person's eating style varies in different settings.

Are obese people 'turned on' differently?

The other area of eating habits in which obese persons were thought to differ is in what turns on appetite. As mentioned in Chapter 4, the leading American psychologist Stanley Schachter suggested that in obese people appetite is turned on by factors external to the person, such as the sight and smell of food. Non-obese people were thought to be more in touch with, and influenced by, their internal sensations such as hunger pangs. This is another interesting theory that has been found wanting. Research has shown that the appetite of everyone, obese and non-obese alike, is very strongly stimulated by external factors. Some people's bodies are particularly strongly affected by contact with food, but these are not just obese people.

The answer to the question: 'Are obese people different?' is no. This will be a more fruitful question to look at when we can clearly identify different groups or types of obese people. People reach the state of obesity by different pathways, and from a variety of causes, and they vary a great deal even in where the excess fat is deposited. It is possible that sub-groups of obese people (e.g. those who are obese from birth, with a strong family history of obesity) may be different from other groups (e.g. those who develop obesity for the first time after some major upset in adulthood) or from non-obese people.

How do people lose weight?

Most people who lose weight do so entirely on their own, without any help from professionals. Whatever self-control is, they've got it. Since most professional treatments are fairly unsuccessful, it is worthwhile to examine 'natural' self-control.

The best researches into 'natural' self-control have been carried out by two American psychologists, James Prochaska and Carlo DiClemente. Their studies of how people exercise self-control over their behaviour show a very similar pattern in each of a range of appetites including slimming, stopping drinking, stopping smoking etc. They found that people go through a series of similar stages of change in the same order, regardless of the habit involved. These stages are, firstly, pre-contemplation, and then contemplation, action and maintenance.

In pre-contemplation the habit is not viewed as a problem; the area is not a 'live' issue, and the concern of others is not understood. The attitude is: 'It's OK; I'm happy the way things are; I'm not trying to change.' Some people never move beyond pre-contemplation, but some move on to contemplation. In that stage the person thinks that there is a problem, and that maybe she ought to change, but she has not made up her mind what, if anything, to do about it. In contemplation the habit is a hot issue, and the person is often seeking information about it, possibly involving reading or talking about it with friends. The attitude is: 'It's not OK, but I'm not sure what I'm going to do about it.' The transition from pre-contemplation to contemplation is often triggered by some event such as illness, getting into trouble with the law, or having one's spouse give an ultimatum to change or leave. Some people contemplate change but decide that it is not for them; others move on to action. In the action stage the person has resolved to do something about the habit and is actively engaged in making changes. In this stage the attitude is: 'I'm doing something to change things.' After this comes the maintenance stage in which gains are actively being consolidated and consciously held on to in the face of events. The attitude is: 'I'm making sure that these changes that I've made stay changed.'

Eventual success follows maintenance and takes the form of maintained changes without conscious effort. A successful person says: 'I don't smoke', rather than as in maintenance: 'I've stopped smoking'; the habit is no longer an issue. And many times there is a further stage of change, relapse, in which the changes made collapse, either suddenly or gradually. The attitude in relapse is: 'I'm slipping back.'

The sequence of changes for weight reduction is illustrated below in Table 8.

Prochaska and DiClemente found that there is a circle of change, like a revolving doorway. People often go through the sequence from pre-contemplation to relapse, but they don't stop there but go back into pre-contemplation and round the cycle of change again. Some can exit as a success after their first attempt, but it is much more common to take a number of attempts (on average smokers make three serious attempts before they become non-smokers). A success would be someone who has stopped consciously controlling her behaviour, and who no longer experiences temptation to go back to her old ways. In the case of weight reduction the more times you go round the cycle of change the harder it can become, because successive diets progressively reduce the metabolic rate, slowing down the rate of weight loss. The unique thing about weight reduction is the very small amount of time spent in pre-contemplation, and the rarity of anyone escaping from maintenance as a success who never consciously controls their weight. Restrained eaters who are consciously concerned about weight (and who were discussed in Chapter 5) are found in both maintenance and contemplation.

Table 8 Stages of change

PRE-CONTEMPLATION	'It's OK; I'm happy with my weight; I'm not trying to change.'
	↓ ↓ ↓
CONTEMPLATION	'I'm not happy with my weight but I'm not sure what to do about it yet.'
	↓ ↓ ↓
ACTION	'I'm not happy with my weight and I've decided to lose some, and this is what I'm doing. . . .'
	↓ ↓ ↓
MAINTENANCE	'I'm making sure I keep off the weight I lost.'
	↓ ↓ ↓
RELAPSE	'I'm putting it all back on again.'

The secrets of success

Different strategies seem to be helpful in different stages of change. There have been several studies comparing people who have been successful with those who have been unsuccessful in losing a substantial amount of weight by their own means and maintaining the loss for some time.

In the action stage the successful weight losers tend to help themselves in a greater number of ways (e.g. rewarding themselves for success, keeping a record of food eaten, exercising) than the others, and go on trying for longer. They tend to start off dieting more consistently and to be rewarded by a higher rate of weight loss. In the action stage successful slimmers tend to use two ways of helping themselves that unsuccessful slimmers rarely employ. One is talking to themselves, directing themselves what to do or not to do by instructing themselves mentally, in the same way that they would direct someone else. This could take the form of instruction, e.g.: 'Don't eat that, you've got to stick to it; don't spoil it now!', or praise, e.g.: 'That was good, you could easily have blown it, but you really did well!' By contrast unsuccessful dieters more commonly report excuses to eat or wistful longing for food, tempting themselves. The second way that successful dieters help themselves in the action stage is by consciously distracting themselves, giving themselves something to do or think about that takes their minds off food. Both these are active strategies in which the dieter consciously and actively takes self-control.

Success in the maintenance stage is more closely linked with frequent weighing and a vigilant attitude towards weight regain. The most successful maintainers give themselves a very small margin for complacency; they regard a regain of about a kilo (two or more pounds) as a cue for actively doing something about it, to bring their weight back down. Slipping from maintenance to relapse tends to occur in one of three circumstances: negative emotions (e.g. depression or anxiety), being with others in a good mood, and social pressure from others to eat. If a slip or lapse occurs in one of these situations it may or may not lead to a full-blown backsliding or relapse; a major factor in influencing what will happen is how the person views what has happened. Viewing a lapse as a one-off event which is a reminder to be more vigilant (as in 'one swallow doesn't make a summer') is more positive than viewing it as a fatalistic sign of inevitable failure (e.g. 'I've got a subconscious need to be fat').

What we have learned about 'natural' self-control has

important implications for professional help or treatment. It seems that different help is required according to which stage a person is in; a contemplator has very different needs from a maintainer and help is most likely to be effective if it goes with the grain rather than against it.

Losing weight by external control

There is a wide variety of methods of forcing a person to lose weight, but none is totally satisfactory. Surgical procedures such as bypass surgery are very effective in producing dramatically large and lasting reductions in weight, but do have a definite risk of death, and usually produce a range of unpleasant side-effects such as chronic diarrhoea. Surgery is a practical option only for the extremely obese. All other treatment techniques attempt to help dieters control their own behaviour. Anorectic drugs are effective in helping to reduce food intake, but once the treatment stops the weight is regained; taking the drugs does not allow people to learn how to manage without them. Jaw-wiring has a very direct effect on eating because it involves wiring the jaws together so that only liquids can be taken in. High-calorie liquids can still be taken! As with drug-taking, jaw-wiring has a substantial immediate effect while the jaws are wired together, but this does not last once they are unwired and the person is eating solid food again. The fact that obese people are willing to subject themselves to this extreme, conspicuous treatment shows how deep their need is to lose weight, and how difficult the task is. People only approach jaw-wiring as a last resort, in desperation.

Attempts to control weight by external influence are effective while that influence is operating but not afterwards. Another example of this is deposit contracting, in which the slimmer deposits money or valued possessions with a therapist and signs a legally binding agreement. This says that if she does not achieve specified agreed weight losses each week (or does not turn up to be weighed) then a certain amount of the deposit will be lost. Once the person enters into this agreement she cannot escape without encountering events that motivate her strongly. When the deposit is important it can help her to achieve large weight losses. Losses continue while the contract is in force, but cease once the contract ends. Unless there is a series of contracts continuing for part of the maintenance phase, there is little evidence that this approach can generate lasting weight losses.

Deposit contracting is a powerful technique and is used by organisations who have decided to force their overweight members to slim. In the late 1970s the New Orleans Police Force stipulated that overweight police officers should lose 2.3 kg (5 lbs) each month. Failure to reach this target resulted in a gradually increasing series of penalties ranging from a written reprimand to suspension without pay. While the scheme was in force the officers lost weight: when it was withdrawn (as a result of civil liberties litigation) weight loss ceased.

Self-management techniques

The most satisfactory means of extending and strengthening self-control was developed by an American social worker, Richard Stuart, in 1967. This involves making gradual changes in eating habits so as to make them more controllable, keeping a record of what you eat so as to increase your awareness of automatic habits, enlisting the systematic help of your spouse, partner, or another important person in your life, and making changes in the way you deal with food so as to reduce exposure to it. This collection of procedures has been called the 'behavioural self-management' approach – 'behavioural' because it focuses on actual patterns of behaviour (rather than thoughts, unconscious wishes, or whatever), and 'self-management' because it aims to help people to manage their own behaviour. Although, as we shall see below, there are specific procedures and guidelines that apply to most people, this approach sees each person as unique and tries to produce an individualised answer for each person's totally

174

individual situation. Research has shown that the behavioural self-management approach is the most effective (non-surgical) way of producing weight losses that last, influencing progress in both the active stage and the maintenance stage. The combination of this and other effective methods of losing weight (such as exercise and very low-calorie diets – preparations that contain essential nutrients but very few calories) produces large and lasting weight losses, and is probably the best form of professional help that the obese dieter can make use of. It is essential that the behavioural treatment continues for some time after the diet ends and the person returns to normal eating. This approach is successful in producing lasting losses because it helps slimmers make permanent changes in their food-related habits so that eating becomes much more controllable.

Changing the way you eat

The first set of suggested changes in eating habits (see Table 7) is designed to help make eating more controllable by slowing it down, changing it from one continuous activity to a series of bursts of activity that are easier to control, and separating it from other activities prone to encourage eating. If you often eat while doing something else (e.g. watching TV) then the two activities can become linked by conditioning, so that when you start watching TV you automatically start wanting to eat; also you can end up paying less attention to what you eat, and getting less pleasure from it. Many of these changes were developed as ways of transforming the 'obese eating style' discussed above. The fact that such a style does not exist does not mean that these procedures are any less effective, in fact they might make the eating habits of everyone (obese and non-obese) more controllable.

There is evidence that these techniques do work. For example, consider slowing the rate of eating, which is supposed to allow natural satiety to develop and thus limit the amount of food eaten. Two American psychologists, Susan and Orland Wooley, tested this by having subjects eat a standard hamburger meal and then, thirty minutes later, eat apple pie for dessert. Half of the subjects ate the hamburger normally and half were told to eat it very slowly. When the apple pie was presented the psychologists measured the subjects' appetite for it by their salivary response (increase in salivation betrays appetite). They found that the appetite of those who had eaten the hamburger slowly was much less than that of the others, showing that the technique does work. The same effect was shown for obese and non-obese persons.

Table 9   Examples of changes to make in the way you eat meals

---

1 Deliberately pause while eating; put down your knife and fork for a minute or two at a time several times during each meal.
2 Put small amounts of food into your mouth at a time, and put your knife and fork down until you have swallowed your food. Chew your food for longer. Eat slowly. Concentrate on the flavour, savour it, and make eating a senuous experience.
3 When you eat do nothing else. Don't divide your attention between eating and some other activity. Concentrate on the taste of the food and make eating a 'pure' experience.
4 When at home eat all your meals in one place, preferably one that is not associated with doing anything else.
5 Always leave some food on your plate.

Reducing contact with food

The second suggestion, to reduce contact with food as much as possible by making changes in food habits (see Table 8), is based on the fact that contact with food and food reminders stimulate appetite and that it is better to prevent temptation occurring than to fight it. Contact with food is a major determinant of appetite in both obese and non-obese persons. Incorporating as many small changes as possible into food habits has been shown to make dieting much easier. The actual changes to make are determined by the individual lifestyle of each person. One of the major ways of coming into contact with food is through friends, colleagues and family members, and ultimate success involves enlisting the help of these influential people. Such people are often present at mealtimes, may be involved in preparing meals, can be involved in other activities (such as exercise) and have more impact than others. Some important changes are listed in Table 10, but the greatest success has come from involving partners (who could be spouses or friends) and training as a couple how to influence the dieter's eating behaviour and strengthen her self-control. Innovative research by the leading American psychologist Kelly Brownell found that the total involvement of partners resulted in much greater success in the long term; changes made at home can continue once the training is over.

Table 10   Examples of changes to make to reduce your contact with food

---

1 Store 'problem foods' in inaccessible and out-of-the-way places; store refrigerator foods in non-see-through containers; take out the fridge light bulb; don't leave food out; store it away as much as possible.
2 Buy groceries from a weekly shopping list, after a meal.
3 Serve up food on plates, rather than having bowls of food on the table; clear away leftovers into a bin as soon as possible (preferably get someone else to do it); give leftover sweets to guests for them to take home.
4 Ask members of your household never to offer you food; if you want it you will get it for yourself. When people offer you food you do not want refuse in a clear and friendly way; for simplicity do not explain that you are dieting and do not apologise. Say something positive like: 'It looks delicious, but I'm absolutely full up.'

Relapse prevention

The final component of behavioural self-management involves looking towards the future. The procedures described all belong in the action stage but continue to have effect in the maintenance stage. However, we need to look beyond that at the relapse stage to see how this can be prevented. As part of a relapse prevention approach individuals need to identify their weak spots, the situations in which their self-control is likely to be under most threat. Most people are only too aware of these, but sometimes it is helpful to look at a list of them such as the 'eating situations survey' in Table 11. This can help identify high-risk situations so that the slimmer can be prepared for them, but it also indicates how difficult dieting will be; the greater your total score, the less weight you are likely to lose. Identifying the situations in which self-control is likely to be at its weakest is therefore important.

Table 11   Eating situations survey

Most people find it harder to control their eating in some situations than in others. In some it is easy, in others it is hard. Decide how difficult the following situations are for you by ringing a number for each situation.

1 Feeling unwell
no difficulty at all   1   2   3   4   5   6   7   extremely difficult
2 Thinking about chocolate
no difficulty at all   1   2   3   4   5   6   7   extremely difficult
3 Cooking meals for the family
no difficulty at all   1   2   3   4   5   6   7   extremely difficult
4 Just after having eaten something you shouldn't
no difficulty at all   1   2   3   4   5   6   7   extremely difficult
5 Just getting home, feeling tired
no difficulty at all   1   2   3   4   5   6   7   extremely difficult
6 Watching TV in the evening – 'automatically' wanting to eat
no difficulty at all   1   2   3   4   5   6   7   extremely difficult
7 Going past a chip shop
no difficulty at all   1   2   3   4   5   6   7   extremely difficult
8 Feeling on top of the world
no difficulty at all   1   2   3   4   5   6   7   extremely difficult
9 Being offered food in a good friend or relative's house
no difficulty at all   1   2   3   4   5   6   7   extremely difficult
10 Cold weather
no difficulty at all   1   2   3   4   5   6   7   extremely difficult
11 Doing jobs in the kitchen – not to do with food
no difficulty at all   1   2   3   4   5   6   7   extremely difficult
12 Seeing food on TV
no difficulty at all   1   2   3   4   5   6   7   extremely difficult
13 Seeing chocolate in a shop
no difficulty at all   1   2   3   4   5   6   7   extremely difficult
14 Watching TV in the evening – thinking about food
no difficulty at all   1   2   3   4   5   6   7   extremely difficult
15 Feeling worried or upset
no difficulty at all   1   2   3   4   5   6   7   extremely difficult

16 Feeling impatient at rate of weight loss
no difficulty at all   1   2   3   4   5   6   7   extremely difficult
17 Walking by a baker's shop and smelling the bread
no difficulty at all   1   2   3   4   5   6   7   extremely difficult
18 Being offered food in the home of someone you don't know well
no difficulty at all   1   2   3   4   5   6   7   extremely difficult
19 Thinking about food you shouldn't have
no difficulty at all   1   2   3   4   5   6   7   extremely difficult
20 Feeling angry
no difficulty at all   1   2   3   4   5   6   7   extremely difficult
21 Just before bedtime
no difficulty at all   1   2   3   4   5   6   7   extremely difficult
22 Clearing away the scraps after a meal
no difficulty at all   1   2   3   4   5   6   7   extremely difficult
23 After consuming some alcoholic drink
no difficulty at all   1   2   3   4   5   6   7   extremely difficult
24 Being tempted by seeing foods in a shop
no difficulty at all   1   2   3   4   5   6   7   extremely difficult
25 Making excuses to yourself
no difficulty at all   1   2   3   4   5   6   7   extremely difficult
26 Craving for something sweet
no difficulty at all   1   2   3   4   5   6   7   extremely difficult
27 Alone at home in the evening
no difficulty at all   1   2   3   4   5   6   7   extremely difficult
This questionnaire can be used to identify the danger areas – you can then take steps to avoid them. Scores can be further interpreted; details are given on p. 200.

Relapse prevention training helps people to isolate the problems to be solved and to equip them with skills and plans to deal with difficult situations when they occur. For example the person whose high-risk situations include feeling anxious could be trained to cope with that emotion by learning methods of deep relaxation, which remove anxiety more effectively than eating does. The problem can also be tackled by looking at the root of the anxiety to see whether this can be prevented (perhaps by learning to be firmer with people who criticise). Slimmers can also be taught how to cope with lapses to prevent them from turning into relapses by preparing a set of instructions which they can apply to themselves after lapses (e.g. 'There's no point in crying over spilt milk, and even less in spilling any more! I've been doing so well, I ought to get back to it'). These can be rehearsed, written down and kept constantly to hand. This, together with a stratagem for combating unhelpful attitudes (e.g. 'I've got to stick to my diet perfectly or there's no point'), is extremely important because research has shown that how a person views a slip is the main determinant of whether it will be an isolated event in maintenance or the transition to relapse. This approach helps to prevent relapse by contemplating it and making plans to deal with 'emergencies', even though you don't want them to happen. In a similar way the masters of ocean liners try to prevent accidents by having high safety standards, but they also have lifeboat drills, so that if an emergency occurred everyone would have a clear plan of action to follow.

The behavioural self-management approach is a complex package of techniques that has developed over the last two decades – it is the most effective means yet devised of helping slimmers to increase their self-control and lose weight. It is most effective when delivered in an individually tailored way to an individual by an experienced professional, but even has benefits when delivered in a fairly standardised format to groups; Weight Watchers increased the weight loss of their customers by thirty per cent when they incorporated some behavioural techniques into their programme.

Conclusions

The most important factor determining obesity – energy needs – is beyond our power to change at present. Therefore, apart from surgical treatments, all methods of slimming involve changing habits, and then maintaining those changes. The approach that has proved most useful in helping people to produce such changes is the behavioural self-control treatment. The difficulty of producing lasting changes in eating behaviour is not surprising, taking into account the many influences on eating covered in this book.

10

Lives disordered through eating

Eating is a central part of our lives, and our eating habits and attitudes towards food reflect all that is important to us. Usually these reflections are not noticed or examined, because eating itself is so commonplace as to be taken for granted. It only becomes an issue when there are problems, and among the most important problems are the eating disorders of those suffering from anorexia nervosa and bulimia nervosa. Although these are disorders of eating they are influenced by, and themselves influence, family life, physical health, appetite, self-image and all other aspects of life. Each topic that we have considered in previous chapters is relevant to understanding, preventing and treating eating disorders.

In such disorders the act of eating becomes the most important issue in life, rarely out of the sufferer's mind, dominating all other activities. Eating, an action that can be enjoyable and spontaneous, becomes rigidly controlled, or almost out of control, or alternates between these two extremes. Concerns about eating and weight dominate the sufferer's mind, so that what goes into her mouth becomes the centre of her life. Anorexia nervosa and bulimia nervosa are two distinct types of disorder, but there are also many people who suffer from aspects of both, making up a spectrum of eating disorders. In this chapter we look at the nature of these disorders, and how they can be treated; we will also look at how far the psychology of eating helps us to understand them.

Anorexia nervosa

Talking to someone suffering from severe anorexia nervosa is a very unsettling experience. Before you is a person (usually a young woman) who is obviously very thin, even emaciated, but who sincerely believes herself to be too heavy. Despite her outward appearance she feels that she is too fat and should lose more weight. The contrast between how she feels and the reality of her physical condition shows what a serious disorder anorexia nervosa can be. Its main feature is an intense concern about fatness, and a desire to become thinner. As a result sufferers almost stop eating and lose a great deal of weight, till they weigh three-quarters or less of their recommended weight.

This drastic weight loss has clear physical effects, such as halting menstruation in women, producing abnormalities in the functioning of the heart and, in some cases, growth of hair on the face and arms etc. The mental effects of weight loss include a distorted view of the body, as implied above; this is called a disorder of body image (the way we 'see' our physical selves). Instead of perceiving themselves realistically, anorexics have an incorrect image, just as though they were looking at a distorting mirror at the fair, which makes them appear fatter. Anorexics, presented with a TV picture of themselves which they could adjust to make look fatter or thinner, were asked to adjust it to make it correct. They consistently made the TV image look fatter than they actually were. Most young women overestimate their size in this way, because of their concern about their shape; anorexics carry this trend further. Young women who think badly of themselves overestimate in this way because society's definition of attractiveness in females is very much based on bodily features, and current fashion dictates that the female form should be slim.

Anorexics tend to lose weight by rigorous dieting, often eating little or nothing. Sometimes they allow themselves small, strictly limited amounts of low-calorie food, but they always eat within very strict self-imposed limits. Most deny experiencing hunger; this seems to fade away after a few days, but some recovered anorexics say that they did experience continuing hunger. Anorexics often take great pride in their successful self-control, subduing the desires of the body, and succeeding at a task that friends and close relatives may appear to have failed at. Attempts by family members to persuade them to eat more often end in arguments and confrontation. Watching someone not eating and 'fading away' is an extremely upsetting experience, but it is almost impossible to force someone to eat. Even while losing weight rapidly, anorexics often take a strong interest in cooking and nutrition, and may go to a great deal of trouble cooking for their families. As we have seen in earlier chapters, accepting food from others is about much more than nutrition, and refusing food conveys many meanings.

Anorexics tend to avoid those foods which they see as fattening, usually carbohydrates. In addition sufferers some- times aid weight loss by engaging in a great deal of exercise, walking around almost continuously, or taking up running. Very conscientious dieting is usually enough, but for some this occasionally breaks down, and they eat a great deal of food, bingeing on it. This can be followed by vomiting as an 'antidote', effectively erasing their act. Bingeing and vomiting (a pattern called 'bulimia' and a feature of bulimia nervosa as we shall see) can develop from being a voluntary act to an almost automatic habit which is hard to break.

Sufferers from anorexia nervosa give a variety of reasons for not eating, and often attribute it to lack of appetite, a concern about health, or a need to be thinner. A less common reason is 'total allergy syndrome', which is a claim to be allergic to everything. If they are faced with determined attempts to control their behaviour and make them eat more (e.g. in hospital), anorexics often respond in an equally determined manner, which is labelled 'manipulation'. Throwing food out of the window and running on the spot are examples. Being very thin is not good for health; surveys show that very thin people have more than their expected share of illness and die sooner than people of average weight. Extreme thinness is as hazardous as extreme fatness. The Duchess of Windsor was wrong to say that it is impossible for a woman to be too thin. Anorexia nervosa is an extreme form of thinness and people die as a result of it; one in twenty of sufferers from this disorder known to psychiatric services dies prematurely.

Who suffers from anorexia nervosa?

Anorexia nervosa is mainly a disorder of female adolescents and young adults. Only one anorexic in sixteen is male. Anorexia usually starts around puberty or a few years later; it is very rare for the disorder to begin for the first time after the age of thirty. Unlike some disorders (e.g. depression) that come and go, anorexia nervosa continues once it has developed. It is much more common among the upper social classes (unlike most emotional and medical disorders, such as heart disease and obesity, which are more common among the lower classes). This class trend follows the pattern of concern about health issues, and habits such as smoking, which are much less common in the higher classes. Thinness is more common the higher one goes up the social scale, and anorexia nervosa follows this trend. Because of this class bias, in the UK anorexia is much more common among girls in independent schools than those in state schools.

Types of anorexia nervosa

Not all anorexics are the same; there are two distinct types, dieters and vomiters.

The first group, dieters, begin as young teenagers, and lose weight solely through dieting; they tend to be relatively introverted and reserved, and are often ill-at-ease in social situations. Such young women are often particularly intelligent and very conscientious about their schoolwork. Sometimes their family and teachers believe them to be too concerned about their studies. Anorexics have rarely been obese in the past and rarely come from families where there is a history of obesity. Anorexics whose disorder begins earlier tend to seek medical help sooner and recover more quickly and completely.

In contrast, the other distinct group (vomiters) begin later (often in their early twenties), and are unable to control their weight by dieting alone. They also engage in vomiting or laxative abuse. When they begin making themselves sick they usually find this as unpleasant as other people would; it requires an act of will, to steel themselves to do it. Yet as they do it more and more, they find that it becomes less distasteful, and they can do it more easily; eventually it happens almost automatically, just by contracting a particular muscle. It can be a habit that develops beyond complete conscious control. Bingeing tends to be associated with certain foods (usually those high in energy) which are eaten only during binges, and become connected with vomiting. Eating them indicates that the person has decided to binge and vomit. This group of anorexics is rather different in personality, much more outward-going, impulsive, and tending to do things on the spur of the moment. They often experience difficulty in controlling their behaviour in other areas of life, and are more likely to drink excessively, take illicit drugs, shoplift, or take overdoses. They are more sociable, but frequently find this area of their lives unsatisfactory. Often this second type of anorexic has a personal or family history of obesity; they have achieved a dangerously low weight despite biological pressure

185

to be heavier than average. The outlook for this second group of anorexics is much worse.

Is anorexia nervosa becoming more common?

Most experts believe that the disorder has become more common than it was twenty or thirty years ago. It is hard to say whether this is definitely true, because over the same period the disorder has been more clearly recognised by the general public, and services have been developed to cope with it. The more services there are, the more people come forward to use them. Nevertheless all eating disorders do appear to be occurring more frequently.

What is the cause of anorexia nervosa?

There are almost as many theories about the cause of anorexia as there are factors that influence eating habits and, as we have seen so far in this book, there is virtually no feature of life which does not affect eating. There is never likely to be 'the answer', one theory that will provide a complete explanation; instead there is likely to be a combination of factors influencing each case, some of which are more important than others.

Social pressure

Anorexia nervosa is most common in societies where thinness is admired and, in the UK, is most common in social classes where thinness is most admired. It has increased as concern about fatness has increased (see previous chapter). It occurs in women because they are under more pressure to conform to a physical ideal. If values were reversed and fat was seen as beautiful throughout our society, anorexia nervosa would almost disappear. As far as treatment for the individual sufferer is concerned, this implies a need to be aware of social pressure and to look at possible attitude change.

Fear of growing up

Anorexia nervosa is primarily a disorder of adolescence and halts or reverses the physical process of growing up. It causes menstruation to cease and prevents the development of a more mature female figure. It is argued that the disorder represents a fear of development, and may centre around concerns about sexuality or independence. According to this argument the adolescent, fearful of becoming an autonomous being, starves herself to slow down growth and 'freeze' the issue, although not necessarily consciously. This would apply especially to young socially unsure but controlled females. Remaining as a child provokes continued caring from parents. This view of anorexia nervosa implies that any treatment should attempt to help the child make the transition to adulthood successfully.

Family pressures

Clinicians have observed that many anorexics come from families with dominating parents, usually mothers. In such families relationships are unhealthily close and the child has little scope for asserting her independence. She can only be 'bad' in a passive way, such as stopping eating, a means of asserting herself and controlling her parents with gratifying effects. Anorexics coming from disturbed family back-grounds tend to have a poorer prognosis. Where family pressures operate in this way help is needed to shift the patterns of relationships within the family.

Biological factors

Rapid weight loss, a feature of anorexia nervosa, is hard to achieve for women with low energy needs, and so biological factors are important. Carbohydrate bingers adapt to (or are sensitive to) tryptophan, so that this affects their mood in unusual ways. As was seen in Chapter 7, tryptophan in food affects the levels of serotonin in the brain, and this in turn affects mood. Tryptophan-rich foods cause sleepiness in most

187

people, except for people who binge on carbohydrates, who experience the reverse effect. Hormonal imbalance is another feature of anorexia nervosa, and some females may be more prone to disturbances in this area than others. It is also possible that anorexics may have a 'normal' weight which is above average. Inside every thin bulimic anorexic a fat woman is wildly signalling that she needs to eat more. Some symptoms of anorexia nervosa, such as overconcern with food, or wanting to eat in private, are symptoms of starvation. They are seen in starving people whether the cause is voluntary or involuntary. Prisoners of war kept on meagre rations reported much the same phenomena, as did volunteers for studies into the effects of starvation. Malnutrition has mental as well as physical effects. Biological factors need to be taken into account.

A habit out of control

Young anorexics start out in control of their behaviour, but gradually lose control; their capacity for choice is gradually diminished. Their dieting efforts are rewarded by immediate success; they have done well where most fail. Their achievements are also usually rewarded by the reaction of friends and family who, except in the final stages, express praise and admiration at their fortitude. But such determined and conscious restraint is very hard to let go. Habit also becomes important among those who develop vomiting, which gradually becomes more automatic. It becomes difficult to reassert control even if one wants to. In-so-far as part of anorexia nervosa is a habit out of control, help for anorexics should incorporate help with reasserting self-control and with changing habits.

Phobia of fat

A phobia is an unrealistic fear, one that is out of proportion to reality. Anorexics have unrealistic fears about fatness; they fear that they are too fat, or that if they put on a specific amount of weight they will become too fat; they frequently have exaggerated concern about the consequences of small weight gains. Such phobias cause anorexics to feel real anxiety if they eat even tiny quantities of high-calorie food. Body image disturbance is tied up with this phobia, and arises out of the difficulty of adapting one's body image to its new low weight. The same is seen in extremely obese persons who lose weight after bypass surgery (mentioned in Chapter 9); it takes several years for people who have halved their weight to shed such habits as avoiding turnstiles or sitting next to someone on a bus. The nearest most people get to such an experience is when they drive a car or van much bigger or smaller than the one they are used to; it takes time to adjust to the new car's dimensions and this shows when the driver has to park, or go through a small gap. The person used to driving an estate car continues to leave gaps appropriate to such a vehicle, even though driving a mini, just as an emaciated anorexic continues to feel fat. Such disturbances and phobias imply the need for treatment to eliminate them.

How is anorexia nervosa treated?

Different theories imply the importance of different treatments. In practise conventional treatments fall into two phases: refeeding to a 'correct' weight and then attempting to deal with more fundamental problems. Weight correction aims to reduce or eliminate medical problems arising out of starvation; many symptoms 'evaporate' with some weight gain. Severe cases tend to be treated in hospital, in a medical or psychiatric ward. Usually persuasion and negotiation are used to encourage anorexics to eat more; in some cases a more elaborate system is used, which systematically employs rewards. The sufferer is confined to a room, without radio, visitors or access to what she wants. These are gradually granted dependent on progress in weight increase. Some experts (such as Hilda Bruch) have argued that such a system would be counterproductive because it replicates the pattern of control within the family, which caused the disorder, and could therefore prove harmful. In fact an experiment comparing this method with conventional regimes found very little difference in outcome, though the reward system proved slightly more effective. Weight regain is often unpopular with patients. As one young anorexic said to the author: 'It's like asking me to give up a prize that I've won.' Sometimes anorexics describe it as being fattened up, and many either leave hospital or comply with the regime and intend to go back to their old ways when the treatment is over.

The second phase addresses other areas of life, social, family, or attitudinal, with help being tailored to the problems that still exist. Difficulties in engaging in normal social life might be tackled through social skills training, where the patient is explicitly trained in those social skills which she does not possess. Where family patterns contribute to the disorder, family therapy might be offered to help shift them in a healthier direction. This form of therapy involves working with the whole family, identifying unhealthy patterns, and helping to alter them. In a similar way patients might be offered, where appropriate (and where available), self-control habit-changing techniques, or cue exposure treatments for phobias (described below), or the opportunity for individual psychotherapy.

Mary Queen of Scots; a victim of anorexia nervosa?

A strong case has been put forward that Mary Queen of Scots was an anorexic. Her father died eight days after she was born and at the age of five she was separated from her mother and taken to live in the French royal court. From then until her early teenage years, Mary was successful and happy, and thrived on the opportunities presented to her. Her life changed noticeably while she was in the care of a dominant tutor, Madame de Parois. She became thin, and she alternated between periods of eating little and eating voraciously, and at the same time developed a pattern of vomiting. Her level of physical activity rose dramatically in these years, and she enjoyed long hours of dancing, as well as frequent hunting and hawking. These patterns of behaviour persisted after her marriage at the age of sixteen and into her widowhood at the age of eighteen. The pattern of fluctuations in appetite, excessive exercise and weight loss could indicate that she suffered from anorexia nervosa, and her relationship with her tutor resembles mother-daughter relationships that many regard as typical in this disorder.

Bulimia nervosa

The term 'bulimia nervosa' was first coined in 1978 by a British psychiatrist, Gerald Russell, and rapidly gained universal usage. Previously, less explicit terms such as 'compulsive eating' or 'bulimarexia' had been employed. Bulimia nervosa is similar to anorexia nervosa, except that a decreased body weight is not necessary. There is an overwhelming concern with weight and a need to control it, which results in a pattern of weight control involving bingeing and vomiting (or abuse of laxatives). Dieting comes first and leads to bingeing and vomiting – usually because dieting is unsuccessful. Bulimia nervosa is a much more hidden and secretive disorder than anorexia nervosa; frequently partners are unaware of it and sufferers seek help only at an advanced stage. Vomiting starts as an ideal solution to the dieter's dilemma. (It is regarded as odd in our culture but was not viewed thus in other times and places, for example in imperial Rome.) Repeated bingeing and vomiting can prove harmful. There are rare cases where people have died after a stomach rupture following a huge binge. A wider range of less dramatic physical damage is caused by vomiting, such as hoarseness and the erosion of tooth enamel by the acidic liquids brought from the stomach into the mouth during vomiting.

A key feature of this disorder is binge-eating. This is not just eating large amounts of food at any one time; it is also the feeling that bingeing is not completely voluntary, but is out of control and cannot be stopped. Further symptoms include feeling guilty or depressed afterwards, and a feeling of having let oneself down. During binges the foods eaten are usually rich in energy, and are ones that the sufferer forbids herself at all other times. They are eaten rapidly, in private, in large quantities over a short period. Binges often occur after periods of stress; eating temporarily blots out unpleasant emotions. Sufferers often plan their binges in the midst of discord or upset. During binges people eat very quickly, without savouring or enjoying the taste of what they consume, which often amounts to several thousand calories. Often eating is terminated by unpleasant physical feelings of fullness; subsequent vomiting removes those feelings and brings relief, even if the sufferer later feels guilty or suffers self-recriminations. Immediate satisfaction has much more effect than delayed dissatisfaction. The main difference between bulimics and bulimic anorexics lies in body-size; the two groups merge into each other and some anorexics whose weight returns to normal become bulimics.

Who suffers from bulimia nervosa?

Sufferers from bulimia nervosa are found among young adult women, particularly those in their twenties. The average age of sufferers is twenty-four, and the disorder rarely starts after the age of thirty. Surveys of large populations of normal women suggest that two per cent of twenty- to forty-year-olds have a severe form of bulimia nervosa, although one woman in five can show some aspects of it. Binge eating in some form is not uncommon, although vomiting is.

What causes bulimia nervosa?

There is a large overlap of theories about the causes of anorexia nervosa and bulimia nervosa because the overriding concern in each case is the same – a powerful preoccupation with weight. Therefore theories about social pressure apply in both cases. Because bulimia is more closely associated with obesity, biological factors probably encourage the sufferer to be heavier than she actually is. Bulimics tend to be older than anorexics and so the fear of growing up and problems with parents are less relevant; poor personal relationships with a spouse or others are more important. The sequence of events involved makes viewing bulimia as a habit out of control very relevant.

Dietary restraint

Laboratory research on normal people with high dietary restraint showed that they are fairly prone to indulge in binges if disinhibited, either by the belief that they have eaten some high-calorie food, or by negative emotions (such as depression), or by drinking alcohol (see Chapter 5). Bulimics and anorexics are very high in dietary restraint; this is almost their defining characteristic. Bingeing occurs in both after similar disinhibiting events. The disorders develop after a history of dieting rather than prior to such a history. Part of the treatment of both disorders involves reducing dietary restraint.

Treatments for bulimia nervosa

Until recent years the only form of help on offer for bulimics was individual psychotherapy, which attempts to deal with deep problems of the subconscious as a way of altering behaviour. More conspicuous success has been recorded with a new technique called cue exposure, which has been developed to help people with cravings for food, drugs and alcohol.

The bulimic binges on foods that she usually avoids; after a while those foods become so strongly associated with bingeing that contact with them induces the craving to eat. The bulimic feels uncomfortable when faced with these foods, and after tasting them is almost certain to binge. The foods develop an almost 'magical' quality; buying them represents a decision to binge, and the sufferer feels increasingly out of control in their presence. Conditioning processes (described in Chapter 4) are clearly involved in the escalation of these associations.

Cue exposure treatment works like this: the bulimic is faced with binge food in safe surroundings for a long period (several hours), and is helped through the uncomfortable feelings that she will undoubtedly experience. The woman who craves chocolate might spend several hours with her therapist, with a plate full of her favourite chocolate and experience very strong cravings or urges to eat. These show very clearly, even in physical responses such as heart rate, sweating, salivation, and even the expansion of the pupils. Such sensations do not last for ever, but soon start to drop, and the person gradually gets bored with the experience; the cravings gradually fade away. Several such sessions reduce the 'magic' qualities of the food, so that the initial cravings are less and the person gets bored sooner. After several successful sessions in safe surroundings the patient can repeat the procedure on her own at relatively 'safe' times when she could not easily binge if she wanted to, for example just before going to work. Finally she would repeat the procedure in 'unsafe' situations. Scientific studies, which measure the physical manifestations of craving, show that cue exposure has real and lasting effects.

For different reasons a similar technique was proposed by feminist therapists such as Susie Orbach (in her influential book *Fat is a feminist issue*). Orbach argues that the appetite of 'compulsive eaters' (of which some are bulimics) has been distorted because eating and fatness have become associated with so many issues other than nutrition. Therefore there is a need to allow one's natural appetites to reassert themselves, and to get back in touch with one's true feelings. She recommends that compulsive eaters who crave particular foods (e.g. chocolate) should not deny themselves but buy as much or more than they want and surround themselves with this 'forbidden food'. Although her reasoning is different to the reasoning behind cue exposure (she argues if you crave something then your body needs it), the aims of both treatments are the same: to eliminate craving for a forbidden food by becoming familiar with it. The evidence summarised in Chapter 2 fails to support Orbach's suggestion that cravings are a guide to needs, but all the work on dietary restraint supports her theory that concerns about weight can distort appetite. An important message in Orbach's book which is contradicted by the evidence is the implicit suggestion that if you are overweight and reduce or eliminate dietary restraint then your weight will fall to a normal level; in fact many people who follow her advice will put on weight. Despite its popularity, Orbach's general treatment approach has never been properly evaluated to see how effective it is.

Changing eating habits and attitude

One treatment approach that has proved itself to be of great value attempts to help bulimics to exert control over their daily eating habits. This approach, developed at Oxford University by psychiatrist Christopher Fairburn, takes several months of regular meetings. Bulimics are initially asked to regularise their eating habits by eating three or four planned meals each day. This has the value of disrupting the pattern of alternate fasting and bingeing, regardless of what is actually eaten. This is combined with education about the nature of the disorder and advice to carry out some of the habit-changing tactics employed in the treatment of obesity (see Chapter 9). Once these initial changes have been consolidated, attention turns to the patient's attitudes towards eating and body size, and to the identification and modification of unhealthy attitudes. Cue exposure techniques are used as part of an effort to reduce dietary restraint, and the bulimic is also trained in problem-solving techniques in order to make sense of, and deal with, recurring patterns of bingeing. This type of treatment approach has been shown to be much more effective than purely psychotherapeutic approaches.

Conclusion

Anorexia nervosa and bulimia nervosa are serious disorders. Our understanding of them, and our ability to treat them, have benefited greatly from findings and ideas from other areas of the psychology of eating. The more we understand about normal eating patterns the less mysterious the eating disorders become.

Postscript

The issues explored in this book were introduced by an imaginary trip around a supermarket. The answers to the questions raised by that trip show that our eating habits affect all areas of our lives – not just our behaviour at the supermarket and at the dinner table. Our eating habits are as much a part of our lives as the food we eat becomes part of our body. When we start to look at them, as we have in this book, we begin to look at every aspect of human nature. There is no part of human life that does not affect, or is not affected by, our eating habits. In this book we have explored some areas, but there are many more we could have looked at – such as the sense of taste, the links between eating habits and sexual practices, food and religion, centres in the brain controlling appetite, and the effect of diet on intelligence. As we begin to look at eating habits with intelligent curiosity, so we start asking questions about all areas of human psychology.

Our eating habits reflect a variety of views of human nature: man as an animal that needs to eat in order to survive: man as a believer, with firm religious views: man as a social creature, affected strongly by relationships with others; man as a species with a past; man as a being that learns from experience; man as an organism affected by chemicals; man developing from a helpless infant to a mature adult, and beyond; man as a maker of decisions; and man as a creature whose choices are limited by biology. All of these views (and others) are valid at the same time. We are the most complex things we know of, and our eating habits betray this complexity.

Although we have touched on some strange and exotic aspects of life, the main message of this book is how extraordinary the ordinary activity of eating is. Once you start looking at habits that were practically invisible, because so familiar, you will be able to enjoy looking at eating with wonder and curiosity.

Appendix

The answers to Table 1 (p. 13)

Taste combinations used in the cuisines of different regions

Taste combination	Region
A Olive oil, lemon and oregano	7 Greece
B Chilli and tomato	9 Mexico
C Olive oil, garlic, parsley and anchovy	10 Southern Italy and Southern France
D Lemon and parsley	8 Middle East
E Soy sauce, chilli, brown sugar and sesame seed	1 Korea
F Soy sauce, garlic, chilli, molasses and peanuts	11 Indonesia
G Sour cream, dill and paprika	6 Eastern Europe
H Tomato, chilli and peanut	5 West Africa
I Soy sauce, sugar and rice wine	3 Japan
J Cumin, ginger, garlic, plus other spices	4 North India
K Rosemary, sage, marjoram, olive oil and thyme	2 Provence

Table 3 Scoring Restrained Eating questionnaire (p. 84)

For each item that you have endorsed with a (b) you score 1, and for each (c) 2, each (d) 3, and each (e) 4. Your total score is your Eating restraint score.

199

Table 7   Scoring Oral optimism and pessimism questionnaire (p. 137)

How to work out your score
A Count 1 for each of the following you answered YES to: 2, 4, 6, 15, 17, 19.
B Count 1 for each of the following you answered NO to: 8, 10, 11, 13. Add the totals for A and B to make your optimism total.
C Count 1 for each of the following you answered YES to: 1, 3, 7, 9, 12, 16.
D Count 1 for each of the following you answered NO to: 5, 14, 18, 20. Add the totals for C and D to make your pessimism total.

How to interpret your score
If your optimism score is 5 or 6 you are of average optimism; if it's 7 or more you are very optimistic; if it's less than 5 you are low in optimism.

If your pessimism score is between 3 and 5 you are of average pessimism; if it's 6 or more you are very pessimistic; if it's less than 3 you are low in pessimism.

These scores are based on a short version of Kline's questionnare. More reliable and valid scores would result from using the complex questionnare.

Table 11   Scoring Eating situations survey (p. 178)

A

Compute your total score by adding together all your scores.

Scores above 110 mean that dieting is very difficult for you and that you are only likely to be successful if you make big changes in your eating habits. Is it worth that much to you? Scores below 50 mean that you are more likely to be successful and will have to make changes in only a few areas.

B

To work out your profile of difficulty calculate the following scores by adding up your score for the items noted.
A: add your scores for items 1, 5, 8, 10, 15, 20 and 23 and divide your total by 7.
B: add your scores for items 2, 4, 14, 16, 19, 25 and 26 and divide your total by 7.
C: add your scores for items 3, 7, 9, 11, 12, 13, 17, 18, 22 and 24 and divide your total by 10.
D: add your scores for items 6, 21 and 27 and divide your total by 3.

Next fill in your scores on the Graph A. An example of someone else's scores is given in Graph B. Your scores show your areas of strength and weakness, the higher the score the weaker you are in that area. You can examine your profile to see whether each area is equally difficult or whether some stand out as being much more difficult than

APPENDIX

the others. This gives clues as to where you might need to concentrate your efforts. Your highest scoring items indicate areas of particular risk.

Graph A

7

6

5

4

3

2

1

your score

A	B	C	D
physical feelings and emotions	mental habits and attitudes	contact with food	habit

201

Graph B

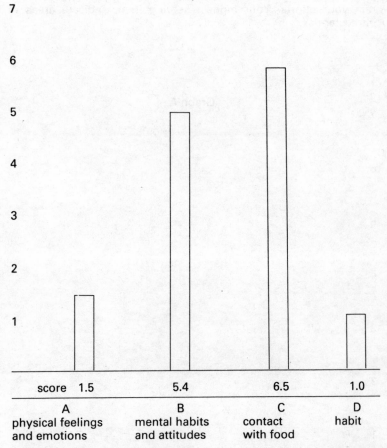

	A physical feelings and emotions	B mental habits and attitudes	C contact with food	D habit
score	1.5	5.4	6.5	1.0

The person whose scores are summarised in graph B has particularly high scores in areas B and C, suggesting that her high-risk areas are related to contact with food and related mental habits. She might need to pay particular care to implementing the kinds of strategies listed in Table 8 and to looking at her underlying attitudes to her problem areas.

References

Chapter 1   Food habits

Bodenheimer F.S. (1951) *Insects as human food: a chapter of the ecology of man.* W. Junk Publishers; The Hague.

Torrance E.P. (1958) Sensitisation versus adaptation in preparation for emergencies; Prior experience with an emergency ration and its acceptability in a simulated survival situation. *Journal of Applied Psychology* 42 63–67.

Woodham-Smith, C. (1962) *The great hunger: Ireland 1845–1849.* Hamish Hamilton; London.

Read P.P. (1974) *Alive: The story of the Andes survivors.* Secker & Warburg; London.

Bavly, S. (1966) Changes in food habits in Israel. *Journal of the American Dietetic Association, 48,* 488–495.

Burgoyne J. & Clarke D. (1983) You are what you eat: Food and family reconstruction. In A. Murcott (ed.) *The sociology of food and eating.* Gower, Cardiff.

Rozin E. (1983) *Ethnic cuisine: the flavor-principle cookbook.* Stephen Greene Press; Vermont.

Coe S. (1985) Aztec cuisine. *Petits Propos Culinaires, 19,* 11–22.

Summers A. & Mangold T. (1976) *The File on the Tsar.* Victor Gollancz; London.

Smith R.E.F. & Christian D. (1984) *Bread and salt: A social and economic history of food and drink in Russia.* CUP; Cambridge.

Baldwin F.E. (1926) *Sumptuary legislation and personal regulation in England.* Johns Hopkins Press; Baltimore.

Hourani F. (1986) Notes for a study of sectarian cookery in Lebanon. *Petits Propos Culinaires, 23,* 42–51.

Mintz S.W. (1985) *Sweetness and power.* Viking; New York.

Anon (1984) Puffers, gourmands, and zombification. *Lancet,* 1220–1221.

Vietmeyer N.D. (1984) The preposterous puffer. *National Geographic Magazine,* 261–270.

Chapter 2   Do we want what we need?

Rousseau J. J. (1762) *Emile.*

Wilkins L. & Richter C.P. (1940) A great craving for salt by a child with cortico-adrenal insufficiency. *Journal of the American Medical Association, 114,* 866–868.

Davis C.M. (1928) Self-selection of diet by newly weaned infants. *American Journal of Diseases of Children, 36,* 651–679.

Fomon S.J. (1980) Factors influencing food consumption in the human infant. *International Journal of Obesity, 4,* 348–350.

Wooley O.W. (1971) Long-term food regulation in the obese and non-obese. *Psychosomatic Medicine, 33,* 436–444.

Porikos K.P. (1982) Caloric regulation in normal-weight men maintained on a palatable diet of conventional foods. *Physiology and Behavior, 29,* 293–300.

Tierson F.D., Olsen C.L. & Hook E.B. (1985) Influence of cravings and aversions on diet in pregnancy. *Ecology of food and nutrition, 17,* 117–129.

Dickens G. & Trethowan W.H. (1971) Cravings and aversions during pregnancy. *Journal of Psychosomatic Research, 15,* 259–268.

Brown J.E. & Toma R.B. (1986) Taste changes during pregnancy. *American Journal of Clinical Nutrition, 43*, 414–418.

Danford D.E. (1982) Pica and nutrition. *Annual Review of Nutrition, 2*, 303–322.

Hunter J.M. (1973) Geophagy in Africa and in the United States. *Geographical Review, 63*, 170–195.

Chapter 3   Learning what to like

Cowart, B.J. (1981) Development of taste perception in humans; Sensitivity and preference throughout the lifespan. *Psychological Bulletin 90*, 43–73.

Weiffenbach J. (1977) *Taste and development: The genesis of sweet preference*. Betheesda MD; US Department of Health, Education, and Welfare.

Mistretta C.M. & Bradley R.M. (1977) Taste *in utero*: theoretical considerations. In Weiffenbach (1977).

Nash S.M., Weaver M.S., Cowen C.L., Davis S.F. & Tramill J.L. (1984) Taste preference of the adult rat as a function of prenatal exposure to ethanol. *Journal of General Psychology, 110*, 129–135.

Lipsitt L.P. (1977) Taste in human neonates; its effects on sucking and heart rate. In Weiffenbach (1977).

Galef B.G. & Sherry D.F. (1973) Mother's milk: A medium for the transmission of cues reflecting the flavor of mother's milk. *Journal of Comparative and Physiological Psychology, 83*, 374–378.

Marlin N.A. (1983) Early exposure to sugars influences the sugar preference of the adult rat. *Physiology and Behavior 31*, 619–623.

Beauchamp G.K. & Cowart B.J. (1985) Congenital and experiential factors in the development of human flavor preferences. *Appetite, 6*, 357–372.

Birch L.L. & Marlin D.W. (1982) I don't like it; I never tried it: Effects of exposure on two-year-old children's food preferences. *Appetite, 3,* 353–360.

Kawai M. (1965) Newly-acquired pre-cultural behavior of the natural troop of Japanese monkeys on Koshima islet. *Primates, 6,* 1–30.

Wyrwicka A. (1981) *The development of food preferences; Parental influences and the primacy effect.* C.C. Thomas; Springfield Illinois.

Watts D.P. (1985) Observations on the ontogeny of feeding behavior in mountain gorillas (*gorilla gorilla beringei*). *American journal of primatology, 8,* 1–7.

Harper L.V. & Sanders K.M. (1975) The effect of adults' eating on young children's acceptance of unfamiliar foods. *Journal of Experimental Child Psychology, 20,* 206–214.

Duncker K. (1938) Experimental modification of children's food preferences through social suggestion. *Journal of Abnormal and Social Psychology, 33,* 489–507.

Marinho H. (1942) Social influence in the formation of enduring preferences. *Journal of Abnormal and Social Psychology, 37,* 448–468.

Birch L.L., Marlin D.W. & Rotter J. (1984) Eating as the 'means' activity in a contingency: Effects on young children's food preference. *Child Development, 55,* 431–439.

Fallon A.E., Rozin P. & Pliner P. (1984) The child's conception of food: The development of food rejections with special reference to disgust and contamination sensitivity. *Child Development, 55,* 566–575.

Rozin P. (1986) The child's conception of food. *Appetite, 7,* 141–145.

Chapter 4   Adults learn to eat

Beaglehole J.C. (Ed.) (1969) *Journals of Captain Cook; Volume 2, The voyage of the Resolution and Adventure 1772–1775.* Cambridge University Press; London.

Garb J.L. & Stunkard A.J. (1974) Taste aversions in man.

REFERENCES

American Journal of Psychiatry, 131, 1204–1207
Barker L.M., Best M.R. & Domjan M. (Eds) (1977) *Learning mechanisms in food selection.* Waco, Texas; Baylor University Press.
Redd W.H. & Anrykowski M.A. (1982) Behavioural intervention in cancer treatment; Controlling aversion reactions to chemotherapy. *Journal of Consulting and Clinical Psychology, 50,* 1018–1029.
Forthman Quick D.L., Gustavson C.R. & Rusiniak K.W. (1985) Coyote control and taste aversion. *Appetite, 6,* 253–264.
Lehner P.N. & Horn S.W. (1985) Research on forms of conditioned avoidance in coyotes. *Appetite, 6,* 265–267.
Pliner P., Rozin P., Cooper M. & Woody G. (1985) Role of specific postingestional effects and medicinal context in the acquisition of liking for tastes. *Appetite, 6,* 243–252.
Booth D.A. (1977) Satiety and appetite are conditioned reactions. *Psychosomatic Medicine, 39,* 76–81.
Booth D.A., Mather P. & Fuller J. (1982) Starch content of ordinary foods associatively conditions human appetite and satiation, indexed by intake and eating pleasantness of starch-paired flavours. *Appetite, 3,* 163–184.
Birch L.L. & Deysher M. (1985) Caloric compensation and sensory specific satiety: Evidence for self-regulation of food intake by young children. *Appetite, 7,* 323–331.
Greene L.S. (1974) Physical growth and development, neurological maturation and behavioral function in two Ecuadorian Andean communities in which goiter is endemic; II PTC taste sensitivity and neurological maturation. *American Journal of Physical Anthropology, 41,* 139–151.
Kretchmer N. (1978) Lactose and lactase. In *Human Nutrition.* W.H. Freeman; San Francisco.
Greene L.S., Desor J.A. & Maller O. (1975) Heredity and experience; Their relative importance in the development of taste preference in man. *Journal of Comparative and Physiological Psychology, 89,* 279–284.
Krondl, Coleman P., Wade J. & Milner J. (1983) A twin study

examining the genetic influence on food selection. *Human Nutrition; Applied Nutrition, 37A*, 189–198.

Watson P. (1981) *Twins*. Hutchinson, London.

Chapter 5 Mind over Mouth

Chang K.C. (1977) *Food in Chinese culture*. Yale University Press.

Taberner P. (1985) *Aphrodisiacs: The science and the myth*. Croom Helm; Beckenham.

Cosman M.P. (1983) A feast for Aesculapius: Historical diets for asthma and sexual pleasure. *Annual Review of Nutrition, 3*, 1–33.

Ruderman A.J. (1986) Dietary restraint; a theoretical and empirical review. *Psychological Bulletin, 99*, 247–262.

Sahakian B., Lean M., Robbins T. & James W.P.T. (1981) Salivation and insulin secretion in response to food in non-obese men and women. *Appetite, 2*, 209–216.

Schachter S. (1971) Some extraordinary facts about obese humans and rats. *American Psychologist, 26*, 129–144.

Rodin J. (1981) Current status of the internal-external hypothesis for obesity: What went wrong? *American Psychologist, 36*, 361–372.

Rolls B.J., Van Duijenvorde P.M. & Rolls E. (1984) Pleasantness changes and food intake in a varied four-course meal. *Appetite, 5*, 337–348.

Rolls B.J., Rolls E.T. & Rowe E.A. (1982) The influence of variety on human food selection and intake. In L. Barker (Ed.) *The psychobiology of human food selection*. Ellis Horwood; Chichester.

Beidler L.M. (1971) *Chemical senses*. Springer-Verlag; Berlin.

Tryg E. (1982) *The perception of odors*. Academic Press; New York.

Logue A.W. & Smith M.E. (1986) Predictors of food preferences in adult humans. *Appetite, 7*, 109–125.

Rolls E.T. & de Waal A.W.L. (1985) Long-term sensory-specific satiety: Evidence from an Ethiopian Refugee Camp. *Physiology and Behavior*, *34*, 1017–1020.

Chapter 6   Can the food we eat make us mad or bad?

Magnus P. (1964) *King Edward the Seventh*, John Murray, London.

Longford E. (1964) *Victoria RI* Weidenfeld & Nicolson, London.

Thorley G. (1984) Review of follow-up and follow-back studies of childhood hyperactivity. *Psychological Bulletin*, *96*, 116–132.

Schoenthaler S.J., Doraz W.E. & Wakefield J.A. (1986) The impact of a low food additive and sucrose diet on academic performance in 803 New York City Public Schools. *International Journal of Biosocial Research*, *8*, 138–148.

Feingold B.F. (1975) *Why your child is hyperactive*. Random House; New York.

Harley J., Matthews C. & Eichman P. (1978) Synthetic food colors and hyperactivity in children: A double-blind challenge experiment. *Pediatrics*, *62*, 975.

Schoenthaler S.J. (1985) Institutional nutritional policies and criminal behavior. *Nutrition Today*, *20*, 16–24.

Egger J., Carter C.M., Graham P.J., Gumley D. & Soothill J.F. (1985) Controlled trial of oligoantigenic treatment in the hyperkinetic syndrome. *The Lancet*, 540–545.

Schauss A.G. (1984) Nutrition and antisocial behaviour. *International Clinical Nutrition Review*, *4*, 172–177.

Gray G.E. (1986) Diet, crime, and delinquency: a critique. *Nutritional Reviews*, 44, Supplement, 89–94.

Pearson D.J., Rix K.B. & Bentley S.J. (1983) Food allergy: How much in the mind? *Lancet*, *i*, 1259–1261.

Rix K.J.B., Pearson D.J. & Bentley S.J. (1984) A psychiatric study of patients with supposed food allergy. *British Journal of Psychiatry*, *145*, 121–126.

Rippere V. (1983) Nutritional approaches to behavior modification. In M. Hersen, R. Eisler & P. Miller (Eds) *Progress in behavior modification 14.* Academic Press; New York.

Chapter 7   Eating, sleeping and character

Webb W.B. (Ed.) (1982) *Biological rhythms, sleep and performance.* Wiley; Chichester.

Horne J.A. (1985) Sleep loss: Underlying mechanisms and tiredness. In S. Folkard & T.H. Mond (Eds) *Hours of work.* Wiley; Chichester.

Craig A., Baer K. & Diekmann A. (1981) The effects of lunch on sensory-perceptual functioning in man. *International Archives of Occupational and Environmental Health, 49,* 105–114.

Aschoff J., Wever R. & Wildgruber C. (1984) Circadian control of meal timing during temporal isolation. *Naturwissenschaften, 71,* 534–535.

Bernstein I.L., Zimmerman J.C., Czeilsler C.A. & Weitzman E.D. (1981) Meal patterns in 'free-running' humans. *Physiology and Behavior, 27,* 621–623.

Green J., Pollak C.P. & Smith G.P. (1987) The effects of desynchronisation on meal patterns of humans living in time isolation. *Physiology and Behavior, 39,* 203–209.

Oswald I., Merrington J. & Lewis H. (1970) Cyclical 'on demand' oral intake by adults. *Nature, 225,* 959–960.

Green J. & Tapp W.N. (1986) Feeding cycles in smokers, ex-smokers, and nonsmokers. *Physiology and Behavior, 36,* 1059–1063.

Adam K & Oswald I. (1983) Protein synthesis, bodily renewal and the sleep-wake cycle. *Clinical Science, 65,* 561–567.

Horne J.A. (1983) Human sleep and tissue restitution: some qualifications and doubts. *Clinical Science, 65,* 569–578.

Hicks R.A., McTighe S. & Juarez M. (1986) Sleep duration and eating behaviors of college students. *Perceptual and Motor Skills, 62,* 25–26.

Hicks R.A. & Rozette E. (1986) Habitual sleep duration and eating disorders in college students. *Perceptual and Motor Skills*, *62*, 209–210.

Oswald I. & Adam K. (1986) Rhythmic raiding of refrigerator related to rapid eye movement sleep. *British Medical Journal*, *292*, 589.

Crisp A.H. & Stonehill E. (1976) *Sleep, nutrition and mood.* Wiley; Chichester.

Evans F.J. (1983) Sleep, eating, and weight disorders. In R. K. Goodstein (Ed.) *Eating and weight disorders.* Springer Publishing Company; New York.

Lieberman H.R., Wurtman J.J. & Chew B. (1986) Changes in mood after carbohydrate consumption among obese individuals. *American Journal of Clinical Nutrition*, *44*, 772–778.

Wright P., Macleod H.A. & Cooper M.J. (1983) Waking at night: the effect of early feeding experience. *Child: Care, health, and development*, *9*, 309–319.

Goldman-Eisler F. (1948) Breast-feeding and character formation. *Journal of Personality*, *17*, 83–103.

Kline P. (1981) *Fact and fantasy in Freudian theory.* (2nd ed.) Methuen; London.

Kline P. & Storey R. (1980) The etiology of the oral character. *Journal of Genetic Psychology*, *136*, 85–94.

Chapter 8   The mark of the past

Harding R.S.O. & Teleki G. (1981) *Omnivorous primates; Gathering and hunting in human evolution.* Columbia University Press; New York.

Isaac G.L.I. (1978) The food-sharing behavior of proto-human hominids. *Scientific American*, *238*, 90–108.

Lee R.B. & DeVore I. (1968) *Man the hunter.* Aldine; Chicago.

Morris D. (1967) *The naked ape.* Cape; London.

Dobkin de Rios M. & Hayden B. (1985) Odorous differentiation and variability in the sexual division of labor among hunter/gatherers. *Journal of Human Evolution*, *14*, 219–228.

Chivers D.J., Wood B.A. & Bilsborough A. (Eds) (1984) *Food acquisition and processing in primates*. Plenum; New York.

Watson L. (1971) *Omnivore: Our evolution in the eating game*. Souvenir Press: London.

Chapter 9   What has eating got to do with obesity?

Garner D.M., Garfinkel P.E., Schwartz D. & Thompson M. (1980) Cultural expectations of thinness in women. *Psychological reports*, *47*, 483–491.

Stunkard A.J. (Ed.) (1980) *Obesity*. W.B. Saunders; Philadelphia.

R.K. Goodstein (Ed.) *Eating and weight disorders*. Springer Publishing Company, New York.

Bennett G.A. (1986) Is there a pathognomonic psychological profile in obesity? *Medicographia, 8* , 22.

Rodin J., Silberstein L. & Striegel-Moore R. (1984) Women and weight: A normative discontent. *Nebraska Symposium on Motivation*, 267–307.

Bennett G.A. (1986) An evaluation of self-instructional training in the treatment of obesity. *Addictive Behaviors, 11* 125–134.

Bennett G.A. (1986) Cognitive rehearsal in the treatment of obesity: A comparison against cue avoidance and social pressure. *Addictive Behaviors, 11*, 225–238.

Bennett G.A. (1986) Behavior therapy for obesity: a quantitative review of the effects of selected treatment characteristics on outcome. *Behavior Therapy, 17*, 554–562.

Bennett G.A. (1987) Behavior therapy for obesity. In Boakes R.A., Burton M. & Popplewell D. (Eds) *Eating habits*. Wiley.

Marlatt A. & Gordon J. (1985) *Relapse prevention*. Guilford Press; New York.

Chapter 10   Disordered lives

Gilbert S. (1986) *Pathology of eating: Psychology and treatment.*
Routledge and Kegan Paul; London.

Garfinkel P.E. & Garner D.M. (1982) *Anorexia nervosa: A multidimensional perspective.* Brunner/Mazel; New York.

Selvini-Palzzoli M. (1978) *Self-starvation: From individual to family therapy in the treatment of anorexia nervosa.* (Trans. A Pomeranz). Jason Aronson; New York.

McSherry A. (1985) Was Mary Queen of Scots anorexic? *Scottish Medical Journal, 30,* 243–245.

Polivy J. & Herman C.P. (1985) Dieting and bingeing: A causal analysis. *American Psychologist, 40,* 193–201.

Orbach S. (1978) *Fat is a feminist issue: The anti-diet guide to weight loss.* Paddington Press; London.

Fairburn C.G. (1984) Bulimia: its epidemiology and management. In A.J. Stunkard & E. Stellar (Eds) *Eating and its disorders.* Raven Press; New York.

Garner D.M. & Garfinkel P.E. (Eds) (1985) *Handbook of psychotherapy for anorexia nervosa and bulimia.* Guilford Press; New York.

Helpful addresses

UK

Action against Allergy
43 The Downs, LONDON SW20.

Anorexic Family Aid
Sackville Place, 44 Magdalen St, Norwich, NR13 1JE.

Food Allergy Association
9 Mill Lane, Shoreham-by-Sea, West Sussex.

Hyperactive Children's Support Group
59 Meadowside, Angmering, West Sussex, BN16 4BW.

Schizophrenia Association of Great Britain
Tyr Twr, Llanfair Hall, Caernarvon, Gwynedd.

The Women's Therapy Centre
6 Manor Gardens, London N7.
(01) 263 6200

Australia

Active Hyperkinetic Children's Association
23 McKenzie Street
(P. O. Box 17)
DONCASTER EAST 3109
(03) 843 6428

Allergy Association Australia-Victoria Inc
P. O. Box 298
RINGWOOD VIC 3135
(03) 720 3215 – recorded information

Allergy Association Australia Inc – SA Branch
37 Second Avenue
SEFTON PARK SA 5083
(08) 269 3130

Allergy Association Australia – NSW Branch
P. O. Box 74
SYLVANIA HEIGHTS NSW 2224
(02) 522 7763
Mrs Jenny Bennett

Allergy Association Australia – Qld Branch
13 Navua Street
STRATHPINE QLD 4500
(07) 205 3113

Allergy Association Australia – Western Australian Branch
52 Dempster Road
KARRINYUP WA 6018
(09) 447 5661
Mrs Hilary Lane

Allergy Recognition and Management
GPO Box 604F
HOBART TAS 7001

Allergies and Intolerant Reactions Association
P. O. Box 1780
CANBERRA CITY ACT 2601

Anorexia and Bulimia Nervosa Fellowship
1 Cookson Street
CAMBERWELL VIC 3124
(03) 813 1352
(03) 813 1180
Mrs Mary Storey

Hypoglycemia Mutual Aid Group (Hymag)
(03) 755 1460
Joan James
Self-help group dealing with the treatment of sugar and other
  food intolerances

Hyperactivity Association (NSW)
24/29 Bertram Street
CHATSWOOD NSW 2067
(02) 411 2186
Meetings; AGM; Parent Support Group (wkly)
Publications: newsletter

Hyperactivity Association of South Australia
18 King William Road
NORTH ADELAIDE SA 5006
(08) 267 5551

Hyperactive Help Association
77 Fernhurst Crescent
BALGA WA 6061
Contact: Mrs D Wells

Overeaters Anonymous
GPO Box 1120J
MELBOURNE VIC 3001
(03) 898 7852

Index

Australia 18, 39, 143, 144, 152
australopithecus 145, 146, 148
aversions 35–7, 62–70, 72–3,
   153
Aztecs 19, 20, 132

babies *see* infants
Bangla-Deshis 77
Bantu people 17
behaviour: diet and 97–121;
   therapy 67, 104, 105
behavioural self-management
   174–5, 177–80
beliefs about food 81–3, 94,
   121; *see also* religious
Bengal famine 8
benzoic acid 111
Beverley Hills Diet, The (Mazel)
   161
binge eating 3, 86, 128, 131,
   183, 185, 187–8, 191–5
Birch, Lean 49, 55
Birmingham University 73
Black Death 15
blood pressure 29, 67, 124, 165
body rhythms 124–9
Bonny Prince Charlie 110
Booth, David 73, 74
bread 13, 17, 65, 93
breastfeeding 32, 46–7, 77,
   133–6, 138
Britain *see* UK
British Medical Journal 128
British Navy 117
Brownell, Kelly 177
Bruch, Hilda 166–7, 189
'bulimarexia' 191
bulimia nervosa 3, 84, 86,
   181–2, 183, 191–6
Burgess, Anthony 12

Burton, Robert 98
bushmen 143, 150, 151
bypass surgery 167, 173, 189

caffeine 131–2
calcium 36, 38, 44
Caligula, Emperor 20
calories: and body fat 31, 163;
   foods high in 75, 85, 115,
   173, 189, 192–3; foods low in
   2, 74, 175, 183; and
   pregnancy 36
Cambridge University 18
Canada 69, 84
cancer 66–7, 165
cannibalism 6, 10
Canterbury Tales (Chaucer) 18,
   82
carbohydrates 65-6, 93, 131,
   183, 187–8
Casanova 132
cassava 93
cats 49, 52, 134
Chaucer, Geoffrey 18, 82
chemotherapy 66–7
children 6, 11–12, 26–30, 38,
   43–59, 75, 81; *see also*
   hyperactivity; infants
chimpanzees 49, 144–5, 146–7,
   148–9, 150, 153
China 7, 13, 16, 17, 21, 37, 77,
   82, 160
chocolate 111; drinking 132
Chrétien, Jean-loup 7
circadian rhythms 125, 126
Civil Rights movement 18
Clark, Sir James 99–103
clinical ecology 116
Coca-Cola 10–11, 131
cocaine 132

218

INDEX